Medi(
Country Wines

Howard Cook

Power Publications

I would like to dedicate this book to my wife, Diane for her patience in being a patient! To my sons, Mark, Christopher and Jonathon who encouraged me to prepare this work and to Mike Power for making me believe I could paint.

Howard C Cook

Ist edition published summer 1993

© Power Publications
1 Clayford Ave
Ferndown, Dorset

ISBN 1-898073-00-7

Publisher's Note

Every care has been taken to ensure the accuracy of all the information given in this book at the time of going to press. Neither the printers nor the publishers can accept responsibility for any subsequent errors.

Illustrations by the author

Printed by Cathedral Print Services, Salisbury

Front cover painted by Joanne Griffith

DISCLAIMER

Many of the remedies and formulas quoted in this book are derived from ancient sources, the author and the publishers make no claims as to their effectiveness or accept any liability whatsoever for errors, omissions or any ill effects attributed to their use.

Contents

	PAGE
Introduction	5
History of Herbal Medicine	12
Equipment	19
Ingredients	20
Sterilization	22
Preparation of Must	23
Fermentation	27
Post Fermentation	28
Bottling & Presentation	29
Recipes – in alphabetical order	30
Alcohol Control Chart	52/53
Wine Making Using Natural Substances	72
Faults and Remedies	73
Essential Vitamins & Minerals of Wine Ingredients	74
Minerals	80
Medicinal Herbs	83
Cosmetics	99
Wine Descriptions	100
Glossary of Terms	101
Trade Label Abbreviations	103
Glossary of Medicinal Terms	104
Index	106

Introduction

Why another book on wine making when so many have been published? Well, this one really is different. Not only will it enable the reader to produce excellent wines, comparable to those produced commercially, but explains in great detail their medicinal properties.

For those who have tried to make wine in one gallon demijohns and ended up with sickly sweet alcoholic fruit juice, the explanation will be found here. Many books on the subject often confuse the newcomer to this ancient and noble art by giving conflicting or contradictory instructions: for example 'You must filter wine immediately it stops fermenting' whilst another book published more or less at the same time states, 'Filtering should be avoided if possible as it spoils the taste'. These discrepancies are not deliberate it is the method each one of them has found that best suited their own particular palate. For one reason or another they may not have found success with another process, thereby deciding through lack of knowledge or incorrect scientific correlation, that the process must be wrong.

The fact is, there are several different ways of preparing and making wine, none of them necessarily right or wrong; they are merely different techniques to obtain different wine types. When applying any of these techniques, however, it is necessary to have a good understanding of what is happening and why, in order to produce a successful quality wine time after time.

On the rare occasions when things do go wrong it will be easy to apply this knowledge to take corrective action and avoid making the same mistake twice, rather than blaming a bad batch on some divine intervention over which you had no control!

From my many years experience in training I have developed this work in such a way as to allow the skills to be acquired by actually making wine. Indeed, even the novice can commence wine making after initial examination of the text and then following one of the given recipes. The intricacies of control and understanding will be developed whilst practising the art and sampling the product.

For those who do not wish to experiment or are not in the least interested in the science of the subject, if they follow the recipes exactly, they will still be able to make an excellent wine, but will be confined to the recipes listed. However, these are quite numerous, and once 'bitten by the bug', the thirst for more knowledge and understanding will undoubtedly follow. I do advise that once the basics are mastered you do experiment and strive to improve batch after batch. Your relatives and wine-drinking friends will be amazed to learn that the quality range of wines they are sampling were made by you.

I would emphasise that the processes described are scaled down versions of techniques used by professional victuallers and commercial vineyards to produce real wine.

Wine is not only a pleasant beverage to consume, it is also an effective medicine, as it contains elements, such as iron, minerals and vitamins, apart from beneficial complex compounds produced by the continuing chemical interaction of the base constituents. As if this was not sufficient evidence to induce us to partake regularly of modest quantities of wine, there is yet another beneficial ingredient and that is the alcohol content.

By dilating the blood vessels, alcohol improves circulation and brings blood to aid the digestive processes in the stomach and thus, by improving digestion, the appetite is enhanced and tense muscles are relaxed.

The benefit of wine consumption in moderation has been known for thousands of years and was widely prescribed by Hippocrates 'The father of medicine'.

The Ancient Egyptians were practitioners of the art of wine making and 'drinkable' wine was discovered in the Pharaohs' tombs. The earliest medicinal preparations by Monks were concoctions of herbs steeped in wine, which not only imparted subtle flavours but also extracted the beneficial drug from the plant which was in turn stabilised by the alcohol content of the wine.

HIPPOCRATES 460–357 BC

A glass of wine with every meal is highly desirable but unfortunately for the majority of us is not economically viable. Now, however, you can produce your own high grade cellar at a fraction of the cost normally associated with wines of this quality for those prepared to spend only a little time in preparation and the patience to wait for the natural processes of fermentation and maturation to be completed. By making your own wine you are able to balance the ingredients to suit your individual palate and those of your friends and relatives, and personal preference is what counts if you are to enjoy your wine to the full.

The steps to setting up and making have been divided for ease of reference into the various stages.

It is not required to read and digest them all before commencing, but it is advisable to read the relevant section at the start of each consecutive stage. Knowledge and skill will come with practice, with the need to refer to the notes less frequently as time goes on.

All recipes are given for a minimum quantity of five gallons (22 litres), as this is the smallest amount likely to result in a reasonable quality. Why produce six bottles of your vintage when thirty can be had for no extra effort and very little extra cost? If you are going to store wine and enjoy as it improves during successive years, then thirty bottles is the minimum required, especially if a great wine is produced when you will wish you had three hundred bottles!

If the instructions are followed, thirty plus bottles of good quality wine should be produced for each five gallon batch thus enabling a good cellar to be built up at very little expense. No punitive taxes to pay either.

Once the basics have been mastered you will then be able to devise recipes, as I do now, according to the availability of good quality ingredients. When experimenting with an established recipe it is advisable to make only one alteration at a time, and to keep detailed records of the making, noting any changes in the bouquet, taste, appearance or other characteristic that could be attributable to the alteration. Leave room to add any further comments when tasting the wine at a later date, say after six months, one year and so on for however long the stock lasts. With experience and the aid of these records you will soon be able to judge when the wine has reached its full potential or when it is likely to reach its peak. Contrary to what some writers on the subject would have us believe, all wines do not continue to improve however long they are stored, and indeed after a couple of years may start to deteriorate. This of course does not necessarily apply to fortified wines as they are in a class of their own. When blending port wine, some vintages may be one hundred years old or more mixed with more recent vintages to impart their qualities on the younger wine.

Do not be too hasty to judge young wines, as often they appear as though they are harsh or astringent to the palate which can cause some disappointment to the novice. When tasted the sixth or ninth month after storing it may not be at all astringent and may have a delightful bouquet. There are sound scientific reasons for this and they are outlined under the chapter on maturation.

If a non-technical person prefers the art of wine making to remain a mystery, then the more advanced explanation can be disregarded. In any case, good luck! and many happy days of pleasure enjoying the fruits (or should I say wines) of your endeavours.

Historical Notes

The history of wine making is almost as old as mankind itself. Archaeologists have discovered that wine was an industry as long as 10,000 years ago. The many references in the Bible and early manuscripts are testimony to the importance wine held in early civilisations. Noah was attributed with the distinction of planting the world's first vineyard and the ancient Egyptians held the skills of wine production in high regard. Many of their tomb paintings showed wine making, and jars of wine have been discovered in several tombs.

It is known from the works attributed to Homer that the ancient Greeks consumed wine as a social beverage, and for its medicinal qualities. As far back as the early Roman empire, there were wine connoisseurs, and records were made indicating the distinctions between various vintages.

During the dark ages, the art of wine making, in keeping with many other skills, deteriorated, and was kept alive only by the monks of that period who required wine for the communion services and the manufacture of herbal medicines.

As it can be seen from the preceeding notes, the modern home winemaker is carrying on an ancient craft. In many ways the modern wine maker is a custodian of the noble art and science, ensuring that the valuable knowledge that has been of benefit to mankind for centuries is never lost. He or she may even be the instrument for maintaining high standards as recent developments in the wine trade of Europe, with chemical additives, are distressing to say the least. Indiscriminate use of chemicals being added to wine is not only undesirable, but

ELEONOR OF ACQUITAINE.

Queen consort of   Henry 2ᵈ of England.

Married 1150.   Died 1204.

An authentic portrait engraved   exclusively for the Court Magazine

VOL XX   Nº 97 of the series   of ancient portraits.   1841

Nº 11. Carey street Lincoln's Inn. London.

sometimes lethal. Other recent practices may also have long term harmful effects on the system for the regular wine drinker.

In the last decade there have been at least three disasters concerning chemical additives to wine with the result that all stocks had to be withdrawn from sale in the stores. Even more disturbing are the fatalaties that have occurred due to these poisonous additions. One incident concerned the use of the highly corrosive and poisonous use of ethylene glycol as a sweetener (the main constituent of anti-freeze). Another incident concerned the use of methyl alcohol to fortify. Drinking methyl alcohol can cause blindness and will eventually prove fatal.

Thus the fact that ingredients can be collected free of pollution and chemical contamination to produce wine of quality must surely be a motivating factor for all serious wine consumers to produce their own. Add to this the benefit of knowing exactly what the wine contains, plus the fact that the wine so produced will only cost a fraction of the commercial counterpart.

Eleonor of Acquitaine

Eleonor of Acquitaine, queen consort of Henry II of England (Henry Plantagenet), is worthy of mention as her marriage caused the demise of the home wine trade, and did much to shape the British taste to those of the French. Her land encompassed the best wine regions in Europe at the time, and comprised part of her dowry to Henry.

A Saxon chronicler writing at the time complains that 'in consequence of the annexation of Acquitaine to England, the importation of wines from Bordeaux and others parts of the South has become immense and the trade of the London wine merchants most flourishing. The land has become full of drink and drunkards. Ordinary wine might be had for twenty shillings per tun, and claret sold at four pence a gallon.'

In Fitz Stephen's account of London he states: 'the two only inconveniences of London are the excessive drinking of some foolish people and the frequent fires.'

The imported wine from France must have been a great improvement on the beverages made at home, for Peter Blois, in one of his letters prior to this period, spoke of the wretched accommodation at the court of Henry 'there is no order, no plan, no mediation, either in food, in horse exercise, or in watchings. A priest or a knight attached to the court has bread which is unkneaded, not leavened, made from the dregs of beer. Bread like lead full of bran, wine spoiled either by being sour or mouldy, thick greasy, rancid, tasting of pitch and vapid. I have sometimes seen wine so full of dregs put before noblemen that they were compelled rather to filter than drink it – with eyes shut and their teeth closed; with loathing and retching.

The fact that superior wines were imported so cheaply to this country meant that home production could not survive such fierce competition and gradually dwindled to insignificance.

The following notes are not a treatise on alternative medicines, merely facts that are recorded for the wise man or woman to try and enjoy. In illness doctors should always be consulted for they have had extensive training and experience in diagnosis. However from observations and experimentation over the last thirty years I have found many 'wine' medicines and herbal wine recipes that are indisputably beneficial to myself, friends and relatives.

Rather than alternative medicines they may be used as preventative 'tonics', or under supervised medical treatment to aid recovery from illness or post-illness, providing the doctor has approved the consumption of small quantities of alcohol.

It is best to emphasize from the outset that increasing the quantities or doubling the suggested dose will have no beneficial effects; quite the contrary it can actually delay the healing process, and cause complications that will be explained later in the text.

It is also necessary to state that although the wine and herbs employed are natural substances, and therefore free of the unpleasant side effects associated with the consumption of synthetic drugs and vitamins, they are none the less in some circumstances extremely powerful drugs so that excessive doses can be toxic and cause vitamin deficiencies.

Alcohol in small quantities, as has already been stated, can be beneficial as a mild relaxant of the nervous system, aid the appetite, digestive function, stimulate the flow of blood, cleanse the body fluids, reduce cholesterol and fatty acids and de-toxify by increasing perspiration.

The consumption of moderate quantities of alcohol is now known to reduce the incidence of heart attacks. It is interesting to note that the high density lipoproteins in the blood carry about 20 percent of cholesterol through the vascular system. Its detergent action breaks up cholesterol and is therefore transported through the arteries without clogging. Moderate drinkers have been found to have a high level of high density lipo-protein in their systems as have women, who tend to live ten years longer than men on average.

The herb agrimony, more commonly known as liverwort, was allotted the name as it was said to cure liver complaints (wort is the early Anglo Saxon name for plant). Recent analysis has confirmed that it does indeed contain a diuretic drug of the same chemical composition as the modern manufactured drug used for the treatment of jaundice, enuresis and cystitis. The latter are all complaints associated with the liver. Willow bark and meadow sweet contain the chemical salicylic acid and in ancient times were prescibed for the treatment of headaches and fever. It is known in modern times as aspirin and is manufactured as acetylsalicylic acid.

There are many more benefits too complex, and to some possibly, too boring to be dealt with at this stage. In other words, in the right quantities it is a wonderful drug enjoyed by mankind for thousands of years. In excess however it is extremely dangerous causing damage to the brain, rupturing veins, depleting the body of vitamins and essential minerals.

When considering that herbal wine recipes have been used as medicines for at least ten thousand years and possibly longer, why are these not more widely publicised and dispensed by established medical practice?

The probable answer is that people can make their own country wines and grow their own herbs and are therefore not under government control. Large multinational drug companies cannot patent them and sell them on at huge profits. The medical profession likewise is concerned to retain its monopoly on diagnosis and treatment, plus the justifiable concern on the possible dangers of an untrained public experimenting on themselves and others with disastrous results. Despite the scepticism of established medical opinion, and the extensive public relations exercise by large drug companies a great many people are seeking out natural cures. A better informed and more enlightened public is beginning to question the drive to be reliant on synthetically manufactured drugs, as are, thankfully, many well qualified physicians.

No one these days can be unaware of the horrifying side effects of several drugs issued in the last decade such as Thalidomide.

Chemically manufactured drugs merely synthesize the isolated active ingredient, which when administered in isolation can cause side effects worse than the ailment it set out to cure.

The latest research however into plant or herbal remedies has proven that the use of natural plants containing the same drug exhibit none of the unwanted side effects associated with the synthetically manufactured one. This has been explained by the possible additional equalizing chemicals or 'buffers' which counteract side effects. These 'buffer' chemical compounds appear to have no active part in the actual healing process but act as physiological triggers to stabilizing processes of the body in counteracting the side effects of the active ingredients.

Perhaps the strangest and to my mind the most interesting phenomenon regarding herbal remedies is the fact that the drug most effective against a particular ailment is one that causes the symptoms of that illness to be exhibited if taken in many instances by a healthy person. Many examples of this will be given later. I discovered this to be a basic law of homoeopathy, *similia Similibus curentur* 'let likes be cured with like'.

Synthetic Versus Natural

As with synthetic drugs, chemically manufactured vitamins can cause toxic reactions, whereas natural vitamins even in quite high doses do not. The chemical composition may appear to be identical under analysis, but synthetic vitamin C is simply ascorbic acid without any other compounds, whereas natural vitamin C from rose hips not only contains ascorbic acid but bio-flavonoids and the entire C complex. It is reasonable to suppose therefore that one or all these additional compounds are the 'buffer' agents to combat toxins or side effects.

Organic or Inorganic

That the term organic means natural is a popular mis-conception. All chemicals containing carbon in their chemical formula are organic. Therefore all vitamins are organic whether they are natural or synthetic. Beware of the term 'pure organic' often used in advertising to promote products.

Potassium cyanide is a pure organic substance but it will certainly have no beneficial effects to the consumer.

They may be pure, they will be organic, but they are not necessarily natural.

Herbal Medicines History of;

Herbal medicine to cure ailments can be traced back to the time of prehistoric man, separately, and in conjunction with sorcery, prayer, music, blood letting, and magical chants or incantations.

The use of herbs as a source of medical treatment therefore represents the most continuous and universal form of treatment throughout history. The study and recording of herbal medicine as a science is known to have been carried out for at least 3000 years BC.

Many herbal remedies are mentioned in the Bible. In Genesis 30, 14–16 Rachel agrees to arrange for Jacob to sleep with Leah in exchange for some mandrakes Leah's son has gathered during the wheat harvest. Biblical scholars have suggested that Rachel desired the beneficial and highly prized mandrake as an aphrodisiac and fertility drug, presumably to be administered to Jacob for the procreation of more children. Jacob and his wives lived about 4000 B.C. so the use of this herb is at least 6000 years. (Caution, mandrake (Mandragora Officinalis) is a poisonous narcotic.

In the written record it is known that the Sumerians described medicinal uses for plants such as laurel, caraway, and thyme.

These original records are now housed in the British Museum in London.

The first known Chinese work on herbal remedies is purported to be nearly 5000 years old and lists 365 medicinal plants.

It is interesting to note that the early Chinese physicians were nearly 5000 years ahead of western medicine in the use of the 'recently discovered' drug ephedrine. It was included in this early work and was derived form the shrub Ma-huang.

From papyrus documents found in Egypt it is known that there were more than a thousand herbal physicians in practice two thousand years before the birth of Christ. Their recipes involved steeping the herbs in large earthenware pots of wine, and they are known to have used opium, garlic, coriander, and mint.

The ancient Greeks and Romans also had Physicians practised in the science of prescribing herbal wine recipes as preserved in the teachings of Hippocrates widely known as the 'Father of Medicine'. Hippocrates the most famous among the greek Physicians was born on the Island of Cos in 460 B.C. Besides practising and teaching medicine at home he travelled widely. His teachings gained him considerable respect and fame and they became the nucleus of many medical treaties by a number of authors from many countries and periods, all of which bear his name. Many of the works were prepared by his sons Thessalus and Draco.

An English translation of 'The genuine works of Hippocrates' was published by Adams in 1849.

Like the early Egyptians many of his medicines were prepared by steeping herbs in wine to extract and preserve the beneficial constituents. The alcohol in the wine preserved the desired drug's characteristics and delayed the oxidation and chemical decomposition of its compounds.

After a long and successful life he finally died in B.C. 357 at the age of one hundred and three at Larissa in Thessaly.

The medicines were dispensed together with advice on correct diet, rest and fresh air to assist the body's own life force. Still good advice to this day!

He is reputed to have treated the king of Macedonia for Melancholia successfully with a herbal wine remedy. The exact complaint suffered by the king is not clear, and may be open to misinterpretation from the translation of his works. From several early works I have observed the term melancholia to be synonymous with the term complaint. Thus in early works the writers have referred to melancholia of the limbs; so a headache may be described as melancholia of the head.

Despite the superstitions and magical pageantry dispensed with early medicines, many ancient remedies have been proven by modern scientific methods to have been properly prescribed.

Foxgloves, used in the treatment of heart complaints contain the drug digitalis (the botanical name of the plant), which is still prescribed in modern times. Similarly the plant rauwolfia serpentine, used for the condition of high blood pressure, contains the drug serpisil.

Theophrastus the Greek herbalist and botanist produced the Historia Plantarum in the fourth century B.C. and is said to have founded the science of botany.

Another Greek physician almost as famous as Hippocrates was Galen properly called Claudius Galenus and referred to as Gaillien by medieval writers, and more commonly as Galen in recent times. Born A.D. 130 at Pergamum in Asia Minor, his father Nicon ensured that he received the best education available. He studied under physicians in Smyrna, in Corinth for a period of twelve years and finally Alexandria. He then travelled to Cillicia, Phonecia, and Palestine practising medicine before returning to Pergamum in 158. He practised for five years before travelling on to Rome. He acquired a high reputation for his remedies in Rome, but as always fame brings enemies, and he decided it prudent to resume his travels before returning once again to Pergamum. His fame had not diminished however, and in 169 he was invited to Aquileia by the Emperors Marcus Aurelius and Lucius Verus. He later followed the Emperor Aurelius to Rome under his patronage. Apart from treating the wounds suffered by gladiators and personal bodyguard of the Emperor, an important part of his duties was to protect the Emperor and his household from poisoning. The concoctions for this purpose were termed Theriacs, and they were manufactured by Galen by steeping herbs in wine. De Antidotis was the name given to the treaties on the subject by Galen. The antidotes prepared must have been very effective, for it is claimed that a senior officer of the Emperors bodyguard, who had regularly taken Galen's remedies, failed in his attempt to commit suicide by taking poison. The final years of his life are obscure but it is believed that he again returned to his beloved home town where he died at the age of seventy. However one Arabic writer claims he died at Sicily at the age of eighty three. No matter which is true, the fact is that he had a long and useful life, and his works were to be taken as established medical practice for many centuries to come. The writings attributed to him include eighty three acknowledged to be genuine, forty five later known to have been forgeries, and nineteen of extremely doubtful origin. In addition Galen prepared fifteen commentaries on the works of Hippocrates.

De Materia Medica was compiled by the Greek physician Pedanius Dioscorides in the first century A.D. and contained details of over 500 plants. The use of plants for medicines changed little during the middle ages as the early Christian church discouraged the formal practice of medicine in favour of faith healing. Many of the Greek and Roman writings on medicinal herbs were laboriously hand copied by monks. The monasteries thus became the local centres of medicine and knowledge and also the source of a great variety of herbs. Many of these herbs can still be found growing in monastic gardens and in the vicinity of old monastery and abbey ruins. In 1510 the monks of the Abbey of Fecamps in Normandy produced a medicine consisting of herbs distilled in brandy. This liqueur was said to possess digestive and anti-spasmodic properties and to have 'prophylactic efficacy in epidemics'. The order was known by the name given to this famous liqueur – Benedictine.

In Europe folk medicine flourished in villages and hamlets, the knowledge being passed around by word of mouth and from generation to generation. Many village 'specialists' gained a considerable knowledge and experience in dispensing medicines from a broken limb to a broken heart. Unfortunately for the dispensers of these cures they often embellished their treatments with special chants, incantations and rituals to emphasize their powers and knowledge to the impressionable and superstitious people. This proved to be their downfall during the witch hysteria and religious persecution of the latter middle ages.

The well known liqueur 'Chartreuse' was also the secret formulation devised by the order of monks known as Carthusians founded in 1084. The oirginal name was derived from the monastery of Chartreuse in S.E. France just north east of Grenoble. After their expulsion in 1093 manufacture was moved to Tarragona in Spain.

With the advent of printing in the fifteenth century hundreds of medicinal and herbal books were published. Thus during the fifteenth, sixteenth, and seventeenth century, the medicinal uses of wine proliferated as the published word spread the knowledge required. Herbals were also being published in Europe in the native tongue rather than Greek or Latin. The first known herbal in England was the 'Grete Herball' of 1526.

No history of wine or medicine could be complete without the mention of Louis Pasteur, French chemist and bacteriologist, 1822–1895. Having obtained his degree as a doctor at the Ecole Normale in Paris, he was appointed professor of Physics at Strasbourg in 1848. It was here that he conducted considerable research on the subject of fermentation, and proved that yeasts were responsible for the fermentation and decomposition of fruits along with other microbes.

His initial work, which led to the study of various yeast cells proved a big step forward to the science of wine making.

The rapid development of chemical knowledge from the seventeenth century onwards led to the introduction of manufactured drugs. The reliance on natural remedies declined in favour of chemical preparations which led inexorably to concentrations of wealth, knowledge, and power for the few specialist makers.

Many well known Herbal treaties followed on in rapid succession but for some reason the use of wine to extract the beneficial ingredients declined apart from the few remaining monastries. It may have been the cost of wine for the ordinary citizen, or the difficulty of supply. Master surgeon, John Gerard 1545–1612, published , 'The Herball or General Historie' of plants' in 1597. A few of his treatments did include the soaking of herbs in wine or beer, as did Nicholas Culpepers. Nicholas Culpeper (1616–1654), produced the herbal 'The English Physician in 1652. He fought the established medical hierarchy, and condemned them for the use of toxic metals and drastic physical measures becoming popular with surgeons and physicians at that time.

Reliance on chemical drugs has been relatively speaking only for a short period in man's history.

Large international drug companies have not had it all their own way in recent years despite massive P.R. and advertising budgets. Their dominance has been challenged by a better educated generation with a new awareness of ecology and man's position in the balance of nature together with a deep concern over recent disastrous introductions such as Thalidomide. This is not to say that all chemical compounds are harmful or indeed of no benefit and all natural medicines are the most effective. Many qualified physicians practise several types of treatment using that which is most beneficial to the treatment of a particular complaint and/ or the patient.

Medicinal wine with herb additives dates back at least 6,000 years and probably longer.

14

Since becoming interested in herbal wines I have read many books on alternative medicine and herbalism, only to find that many of the remedies given and the claims made for them were highly exaggerated and I was disillusioned to learn that many of the books contained a hotch-potch of accupuncture, herbalism, physco-therapy, massage etc, or indeed anything which was fashionable and fitted the bill adequately, for there could be no scientific evidence to prove the case one way or another. One book on treating serious disorders quotes from the teachings of Hippocrates who used a medicinal concoction of herbs in wine and then in a later paragraph attacks the use of wine even in small quantities. Indeed this seemed to be a pattern in many books on alternative medicines and herbalism to alcoholic drink in any form, the great demon to be avoided at all costs. It is best to put the contents of this work in its true context. I am not advocating that drinking wine in large quantities cannot cause harm, it can. It is well known that it has depressant effects on the brain and can reduce vitamin levels in the blood stream. Almost all beneficial drugs taken in excess act as poisons as does alcohol: there can be no justification for banning them all for this reason. To take those authors' arguments, the asprin tablet to relieve a headache should be banned as swallowing a full bottle or packet would be fatal.

Wine as a medicine and spiritual symbolism is interwoven in man's history. It is a pity that so many bigots choose alcohol as the great evil to be avoided at all times. The Son of God approved of wine drinking and indeed used it as the most important religious symbol of all time. Ancient Egyptian Pharoahs had their favourite vintages buried with them for comfort and medicine in the next life.

In Great Britain the progress of pharmacy is only known with accuracy from the early 16th century. The first Medicinal Act of Parliament was passed in 1511, whereby the first faculty of medicine was vested into one body of practitioners engaged in medicine, surgery and pharmacy. Physicians availed themselves of the medicines prepared by Apothecaries (the dispensers) who gradually became knowledgeable about the treatment of diseases and then began to treat patients on their own account much to the dismay of the Physicians. In 1540 an Act of Parliament attempted to redress the balance of giving physicians the right to enter the houses of apothecaries in London 'to search, view, and see the apothecaries wares, drugs and stuffs and to destroy such as they found corrupt or unfit for use'. In 1553 the rights of 'Search and Destruction' was extended to any premises making any sort of medicinal wares of lotions.

However the apothecaries still continued to prosper to such an extent that in 1694 the physicians established dispensaries of their own. The assistants employed and instructed at these institutions were the forerunners of the modern day chemists.

The popularity of the pharmacists with the faculty of the physicians changed the fortunes of the apothercaries to such an extent that in 1793 the latter endeavoured by 'Act of Parliament' to retain for themselves the right of dispensing medicines which unfortunately for them failed.

In 1841 the chemists strengthened their position by founding a society known as 'The Pharmaceutical Society of Great Britain'. This, by now powerful society, obtained its first Act of Parliament whereby the title of Pharmaceutical Chemist or Druggist was confined to the use of its members. A second pharmacy act of 1864 clinched their monopoly on dispensing whereby for the protection of the public the retail sale of poisonous substances was confined to members of the Society. As if to rub salt into the wounds of the apothecaries, physicians continued to use their symbols and measures when prescribing.

The following abbreviations used by medicinal practitioners in writing their prescriptions are for solids:

Gr = 1 grain
ℨ = a scruple of 20 grains
℥ = a drachm of 60 grains
℥ = an Apothecaries ounce of 480 grains

and for liquids

m = minim (1/60 of a fluid drachm)
Gtt = gutta – one drop
cochl = cochléare – spoonful
cochl mag = cochléare magnum – tablespoonful
cochl parv = cochléare parvum – teaspoonful
i = one
ss = seminse – half
áá = of each
g.s.i = quantum sufficient – as much as is necessary.

It is interesting to note that right up to the time of the Second World War pharmacy relied on the farming of plants for its preparations. In a book published in 1933 on the manufacture of pharmaceutical preparations it stated 'From the farm to the factory is but a step and pharmacy on a manufacturing scale is the result'. The Pharmacist was dependent on the liberality of nature and attempted to gain a sufficiency of them by widespread searching and collection. This practice has given place to large farms where important medicinal plants, such as Belladona, Henbane, and Digitalis (Foxglove) and such aromatic herbs as Fennel and Anise are cultivated on a very large scale with great advantage as to quality and quantity. In the same way plants which cannot be raised in the British Isles are cultivated abroad, two of the most important being the opium poppy (Papaver Sonniferan) and Cinchona trees (Cinchona Succirubra) the bark of which yields the valuable drug quinine and for which immense tracks of land are under cultivation in the temperate regions of India, Java and South America'

'In many instances, as in the cases of ergot and digitalis, it is not possible in the present state of our chemical knowledge to value a preparation by analysis, recourse is therefore made to physiological testing i.e. by experimenting upon the lower animals such as the guinea-pig and the barn-door cock. This method is not recognised by the British Pharmacopoeia but nevertheless is commonly accepted as proof of quality. Aromatic waters such as dill and peppermint, are made by distillation with water of the drug or volatile oil; while certain spirits especially "spirits of Sal volatile", are prepared by the same process. Ointments which were formerly made by stirring the medicament into the melted ointment basis are now made by a cold process. The active ingredients, zinci oxidum (zinc oxide) or acidium boricum (boracic acid), being mixed with the ointment-basis in a special mill giving a product so free from gritty particles that one is often in doubt as to the presence or absence of the active ingredient.'

Note their reference to the 'present state of our chemical knowledge' it is amazing to think that this work was published only sixty years ago, when considering the present state of almost instantaneous analysis of complex chemical compounds. It is a great pity that the comparatively recent rush into the technological era has made us solely reliant on machines and specialists to direct our lives. So much so that self treatment and knowledge of the beneficial plants that surround us are lost and the folk knowledge once passed from one generation to another has disappeared apart from the few remaining isolated populations that exist today. It is to these 'primitive' tribes that we have had to turn once again in order to regain some of that 'lost knowledge.'

In the forest of Brazil the South American Indian has maintained a wealth of medicinal knowledge having a plant for all his needs. Self sufficiency in food, plants for every ailment affecting himself or his family and relatives – even poisonous plants to assist his hunting. These so called 'primitives' have now become the 'teachers' as the large drug companies and those working in the field of scientific research are funding many expeditions to these peoples in order to gain new drugs. Their pharmacy surrounds them to be taken free, quite instinctively and naturally, when ever the need arises just as we might pick fruit from our garden.

Medicinal wine on its own or in conjunction with herbs, cannot be described as alternative medicine, rather they are the original medicants used throughout man's history.

Their use, to cure ailments, can be traced back to ancient history, organs of animals, (including humans), blood letting, magical chants and incantations.

The use of wine and herbs as a source of medical treatment therefore represents the most continuous and universal form of treatment throughout history. Much of the 'witchcraft' and superstitions having been dispensed with, although not entirely as described later in the text.

The use of wine and herbal remedies is known to have existed for at least one hundred and twenty centuries before the birth of Christ. The study and recording of herbal medicine as a separate science is known to have existed for at least fifty centuries B.C., and probably longer although to date no records have been found to substantiate it prior to this.

The grape has existed for millions of years, so it may be assumed that earliest man, gathering and storing wild fruits and the juices, probably discovered the phenomena of fermentation. One can only imagine the effect on a primitive and superstitious mind.

Apart from the narcotic action the assimilation of beneficial ingredients and the assistance in digestion of protein in a poor diet, would undoubtedly lead to the assumption of mystic or spiritual properties.

It is known from archeological excavations that wine was produced in quantity as far back as one hundred centuries B.C. A study of these accumulations of pips, and the use of carbon dating techniques has revealed that wine was being produced from cultivated vines as far back as eight thousand years B.C. (Carbon dating is based on the amount of radiation present in the carbon atom. The amount of radiation decreases with age from the organic sample, so by measuring the radiation level at any one time it is a simple enough task to plot backwards to establish the approximate date the compound was first formed, in this case the grape pip.).

As there would have been a considerable period of time for a cultivar to be produced from the wild vine it can be assumed that wine was made long before this period. It also indicates that wine was held in esteem for precious labour to be used in the selection and care of vines.

The wild vines need a male and female variety to cross pollinate, only a few would have been found to be self fruiting, and the vast majority of these would have produced a lower yield of grapes. There must have been considerable effort, in a trial and error basis, over many years to arrive at a self pollinating variety bearing a reasonable yield,

Wine thus became interwoven in mankinds history as a medicine, a spiritual symbol and as an accompaniment to celebrations, from birth to marriage and finally the grave.

ELDERBERRY WINE

STAGE 1
Clean and sterilize utensils then assemble ingredients (SEE RECIPE)

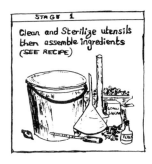

STAGE 2
prepare fruit
Strip from stalks using a sterilized (silver) fork

STAGE 3
measure ingredients & start yeast

STAGE 4
Add cooled boiled water to fruit in preparation vessel

STAGE 5
Boil water, and while still warm, add other ingredients (except yeast) to dissolve.

STAGE 6
Add ingredients. When must temperature reaches 65°F introduce yeast while stirring with wooden spoon gently plug preparation vessel

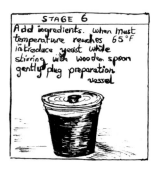

STAGE 7
wait until vigorous fermentation and frothing ceases Then syphon off into fermentation vessel Discard lees (solids)

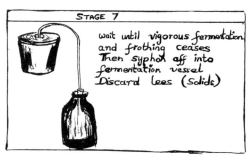

STAGE 8
Adjust S.G. to required level (use sugar syrup as required)

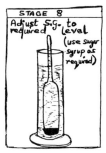

STAGE 9
check S.G. periodically when S.G. reaches 1·00, Add four Campden tablets & Bentonite

Leave for a week Wine should be crystal clear

STAGE 10
Filter into Storage vessels

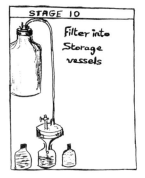

STAGE 11
Bottle using Sterilized equipment and bottles Then label & add foils.

STAGE 12
Rack making sure wine touches the cork

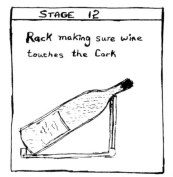

Equipment

The equipment listed, provides all that is necessary to start making your wine immediately. The equipment can be extended to produce even larger batches at a later date should your endeavours make you more ambitious. Remember however when you start brewing in 100 gallon lots, you must not sell your wines without the necessary legislative approvals from H.M. Customs & Excise and local magistrates. You may not even offer a bottle, albeit free of charge, for the purpose of a raffle, however good the cause may be. Whilst on the subject of the law it is as well to mention that the distillation of wine to obtain spirit is a crime for anyone not licenced to do so. In any case it is a dangerous exercise, without special equipment and knowledge, for the inexperienced to undertake.

Your equipment should contain the following:

1. Vessel for must preparation

2. Fermentation vat with an airlock

3. Thermostatically controlled heater

4. Measuring jug

5. Hydrometer

6. Bottling machine (corking implement, or flogger)

7. Nylon brush

8. Filtration equipment

9. Labels

10. Straight sided corks

11. Storage and maturation containers

12. Funnel

Ingredients

There are some schools of thought that say wine can be produced only from the grape, and only those beverages should be called wines. On the other hand advocates of fruit and flower wines or 'Country Wines' claim they can imitate the commercial grape wine by control of ingredients and blending. Furthermore there are several books on the market which promote the concept of making wine with a combination of grape juice and country wine ingredients. As already stated this only goes to show that tastes differ.

It is true that the grape contains all the necessary constituents for fermentation, such as sugar, tannin, acids, and nutrients in balance. Once we have gained an understanding of those constituents we can balance the must to make up any deficiencies inherent in the base material, thus producing excellent wine from elderberries and other ingredients usually associated with country wine. The latter ingredients have the advantage, in this country anyway, of being readily available and items such as elderberry, blackberry and a host of other items can be collected for free. Hence sixty bottles of excellent wine can be obtained for the price of nine bags of sugar plus a few minor additions such as corks and labels.

As the purpose of this book is to assist in the building up of a cellar suited to individual taste and a relatively small group of friends, it is not necessary to consider the arguments as there are no commercial considerations at this stage. I would advise however that tastings of commercial wine for comparison are carried out from time to time, even if it only improves the ego when your wine is adjudged superior to the commercial type. The various ingredients are described here but it is not necessary to study this section in detail before commencing your making.

You can start wine making following one or other of the recipes given. There are both grape and country wine recipes plus mixtures of the two and I will leave it to the reader to decide which is preferred after trial without entering into the controversy. All the recipes are tried and tested and should prove successful with every batch, and whatever the choice will make a quality wine to give years of pleasure, perhaps building a comprehensive cellar for your children to inherit or perhaps even grandchildren to appreciate.

Grape Concentrates

Only good quality grape juice will produce a quality wine. The concentrated grape juice should be one that has had water removed by the vacuum process, not a process involving the application of heat, as the latter will destroy many of the beneficial qualities. It is also best to avoid cheap blends gathered from inferior vineyards.

The consequence and purpose of removing the water reduces the bulk for ease of transportation and at the same time produces such a high concentration of sugar that it cannot ferment in storage. Suppliers of grape concentrates often advertise them in wine types, such as, port type, sauternes type, and so on. The concentrate has already been adjusted by the supplier in this case, so having decided what type of wine is required it is only necessary to purchase the appropriate type, replace the water that existed prior to concentration and commence the fermentation process as the instructions prescribe.

Initially it is best to follow the supplier's instructions, but once more experienced you may choose to vary the constituents and or method to suit your own tastes.

The ingredients for other types of wine are listed in the section preparation of musts (the prepared liquid about to be fermented).

The following list is of other ingredients you will eventually require, especially if you are going to experiment. Most reputable stockists of wine-making equipment, or beer-making suppliers, should have all these items.

You will need:

1. Acids
   (a) Citric
   (b) Malic
   (c) Lactic
   (d) Tartaric
2. Grape tannin
3. Pectin-destroying enzyme (Pectozyme).
4. Starch-reducing enzyme
5. Finnings e.g. Bentonite
6. Sterilizing compound e.g. sodium metabisulphite
7. Sugar
8. Yeast nutrient
9. Yeast (according to wine)
10. Potassium Sorbate (wine stabilizer stops any secondary fermentation, not recommended for champagne.)

Sterilization

Most problems associated with wine making and spoilage is now understood due to considerable research, and is attributable mainly to incorrect sterilization of equipment and ingredients. It must be stressed here that sterilization of all equipment whether (or not) it comes into contact with the wine is a necessary chore and should not be skimped however clean the equipment may appear to be. You are dealing with micro-organisms undetectable to the human eye, that is, unwanted bacteria and undesirable strains of yeast always present in the air. What appears to be a sparkling clean surface may in fact contain many living forms just waiting for the ideal conditions to multiply in your carefully assembled ingredients or must.

Having said this, it is quite a simple matter to ensure that all articles are free of these pests and of all contamination, providing you follow the methods described.

Do not rely on boiling water for sterilization as advocated in many books: it is not satisfactory, and in the act of using it for attempted sterilization you will only destroy useful vitamins, flavours and oils, but not the harmful bacteria.

There are several proprietary brands of sterilizer for sale, sodium metabisulphite being the most widely used and often sold in the tablet form as Campden tablets. If using sodium metabisulphite it is most economical to make up a concentrated solution from the powdered form and store in a sealed dark bottle. This is then readily diluted in a known quantity when required. If sterilizing a 5 gallon container the addition of two teaspoonfuls of citric acid will make an efficient cleaner for the removal of stains.

Always sterilize equipment when storing even though it will again be sterilized before subsequent use.

Milton, used for the sterilization of babies' feeding equipment, or similar products are often used as they have no corrosive properties and the solution does not leave deposits, or tide marks, common with many brands now on the market. Another plus is that the vessel does not have to be rinsed with water after sterilization therefore avoiding the risk of reintroducing water-borne bacterial infection. Whatever the brand chosen, adequate instructions are supplied with the product for the correct use and dilutions, so it is not necessary to list here the various ways of preparing, using and storing.

A systematic routine of sterilizing equipment and materials directly before and after use will ensure trouble free working and is well worth the small effort required.

Preparation of Must

There are seven main types of ingredients from which wine may be produced either on their own or in combination.
These are:

1. Grapes or grape juice concentrate or dried grapes
2. Fruit (fresh, dried, bottled or frozen)
3. Tropical fruit juices (with no added preservatives)
4. Flower blossom (fresh or dried)
5. Vegetables
6. Cereals
7. Honey (Mead)

The enormous range of materials available to the home wine maker means that an infinite variety of wines can be produced all the year round taking advantage of obtaining supplies when they are most plentiful and therefore cheapest. Thus a wide variety of tastes and blends is available to the enthusiastic maker willing to accept the excess produce of fruits, flowers and vegetables of his neighbours and relatives, especially if in return they receive some of their unwanted over-production in liquid form.

It is probably worth mentioning that the wine produced from some of the above ingredients will often have none of the flavour usually associated with it while in its natural state. When flavour extraction is mentioned I do not mean that we are making a beverage with for instance strawberries, to produce a flavour resembling strawberry juice. It is merely that the berries will impart some of their particular characteristics and aromas which in the matured wine will not necessarily bear any resemblance to the original flavour.

There are six major methods of must production available to the non commercial maker. They are:

1. Infusion
2. Direct fermentation
3. Sugar extraction
4. Carbonic maceration
5. Pulp fermentation
6. Soaking in water

Do not boil ingredients as apart from the disadvantages mentioned earlier you run the risk of imparting unwanted and undesirable flavours, cause extra pectin and destroy delicate volatile oils, vitamins and other beneficial constituents.

Pulp fermentation and soaking in water have, by experience over many years of making, proved the most reliable methods, producing consistently good results.

Infusion

Is used in the preparation of flower wines in order to preserve the delicate scents and oils which impart both bouquet and flavour to the finished product. There are two methods of infusion:

(a) One is to soak the flowers or petals in cold water for three days then add the liquid to a neutral grape or fruit must. A neutral must is one lacking in strong flavours and is employed so as not to mask the light flavour of the flower.

(b) The alternative method is to hang a nylon or muslin bag (a sterilized pair of tights will do), containing the chosen blooms in an already fermeneted neutral must. The advantage of the latter method is that all solids are easily removed without straining or the use of equipment, and secondly the strength of flavour is more easily controlled by varying the time of immersion of the ingredients.

INFUSION OF HERBS OR FLOWERS

Direct Fermentation

Pure fruit juices without additives or preservatives are now readily available and relatively inexpensive especially at certain discount stores and health food shops.

The juice so purchased is ready to go straight into the fermentation stage without any fuss or mess. By buying juices in this way there is no need to buy a fruit press, which is expensive and many of them are so poorly constructed that they are a waste of money.

Some kitchens may boast an electric juice extractor amongst their appliances. If you are able to have the use of one of these appliances, then you can take advantage of a glut of fruit in the garden. It is possible to utilise any spare capacity in the freezer to store an over abundance of fruit to be fermented at another time when ingredients are not readily available.

As the juice is free, apart from your labour, the cost per bottle is very cheap indeed.

Sugar Extraction

A method of juice and flavour extraction when prolonged soaking or pulp extraction is undesirable. For example, when making rhubarb wine it will keep the harmful oxalic acid down to an acceptable level. The method is to chop up the fruit and cover with the sugar from the recipe. Mix thoroughly and leave for two days keeping well covered, after which time the juice from the fruit will have soaked into the sugar to form a thick syrup which can then be strained into the preparation vessel. Wash the pulp in cold water to remove remaining syrup and strain into preparation vessel. The acidity balance can then be adjusted, after which the other ingredients such as yeast, nutrient, water, sultanas or raisins (if required), pectic enzyme and finally yeast, when must is warmed to working temperature.

If using Campden tablets to sterilize the must and to inhibit discolouration by oxidation, then there must be an interval of twenty-four hours between their addition and that of the other ingredients. In any case when adding pectic enzyme to a must it is prudent to leave the must for six hours before warming to add the yeast, as temperature increase will inhibit the enzyme in its action.

Carbonic Maceration

A wine making technique developed in California. The grapes or fruit are stored in an atmosphere of carbon dioxide (CO_2). During this process more sugar is developed in the grape and the natural enzymes on the skin of the fruit commence complex chemical breakdown of the grape different in nature from those encountered with pulp fermentation. The tannin content is greatly reduced by this method. The juice is extracted by the standard method of pressing.

When used with red fruits such as elderberry, or blackberry, more flavour is extracted so less fruit is required in the preparation of the must and the maturation time is reduced. The home wine maker can simulate this process by placing the fruit in a near airtight container after sterilization and displacing the air with carbon dioxide fed in by a tube from a batch of wine already fermenting or by suspending the fruit in a bag above a yeast starter to provide the carbon dioxide. If the latter is used make sure there is adequate facility for allowing excess carbon dioxide to escape through a vent.

Pulp Fermentation

The major wine recipes in this book employ this technique. Unlike many books describing this method, do not use boiling water. In certain works on the subject which state that boiling water is necessary for sterilization, it is obvious that the author knows very little of bacteriology.

The fruit is sterilized at the start so that fermentation stages can commence within twenty-four hours, and because alcohol is produced which is in itself a strong disinfectant together with a layer of carbon dioxide above the must (which should be kept well covered) there is virtually no risk of airborne infection. Enough has been said on the risks of using boiling water, and if used on cereal grains it will extract far too much starch which is undesirable except in the case of special starch ferments with a certain 'starch yeast'. **Boiling water also renders Campden tablets useless**.

After the fruit has been fermenting in the preparation vessel at a constant temperature indicated in the receipe for five days, the juice is strained from the solids into the fermentation vessel.

By using the pulp fermentation process it is not necessary to invest in an expensive wine press as all the colouring, flavour, and nutrients are extracted aided by the leaching effect of the alcohol produced in the initial ferment.

Soaking Method

In this method the constituents are lightly rinsed in cold previously boiled water to clean, then placed in preparation vessel just covered in water to which the sterilizing agent has been added. The constituents are then stirred vigorously each day for a period varying from three days to seven days according to recipe. Once the fruit has broken down to release its juices it is then strained from the solids into fermentation vessel.

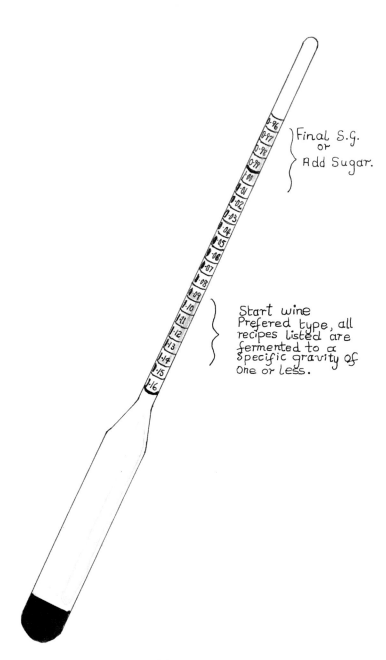

Final S.G.
or
Add Sugar.

Start wine
Prefered type, all
recipes listed are
fermented to a
specific gravity of
One or less.

Fermentation

Thankfully, it is not necessary to understand fully the chemistry of the process to be able to control all aspects during wine production. Some knowledge is essential however and the following chapter should enable anyone to control the quality, speed of ferment, and final alcohol content of his or her batches.

Fast wine and three week brews are not good wines, it is necessary to emphasise that a good slow ferment is desirable. Good wine takes time, and should after all be a leisurely pursuit, not a race against the clock. Time and patience are necessary to the production and final maturation of good quality wine.

Having prepared the must using one of the recipes, the next step is to monitor the progress of fermentation by use of a HYDROMETER.

The hydrometer is not a mystical or complicated scientific instrument. Nothing could be further from the truth. The instrument works on the simple principal that articles float higher in denser liquids than they will in pure water.

The measurements indicated on the instrument refer to the specific gravity of the solution, i.e. the amount of dissolved solids such as sugar in the water. Water has a s.g. (specific gravity) of 1.00, so as sugar is added the s.g. increases. Alcohol has an s.g. less than water so that as the sugar ferments and turns to alcohol the s.g. decreases back towards 1.00, at which point it is usual to stop the fermentation process.

It is undesirable to allow fermentation to proceed beyond this point as the process may be at the expense of the wine content. Many hydrometers today contain colour bands as shown in diagram. The sugar is added until the appropriate colour band is reached for the batch to be made depending on whether it is for a dry, medium or sweet wine. The fermentation process is then allowed to proceed to the mark indicated, thus allowing the sweetness and alcohol content to be carefully monitored.

The table on pages 52 and 53 provides a quick reference chart that makes the measurements with the hydrometer easy, and also acts as an automatic ready reckoner to chart the progress of fermentation.

The initial first stage fermentation which is most vigorous (anaerobic stage) lasts approximately seven to ten days. The first action of the enzymes produced by the yeast is to convert the granulated sugar to invert sugars. Honey is a naturally occurring form of invert sugar. As the latter is expensive, household sugar can be converted to invert prior to fermentation. A quantity of invert sugar in the syrup form is useful when adding sugar to a fermenting wine or when gradually 'feeding' in the latter stages to maximise alcohol formation.

To convert 2 lbs. of granulated sugar, add ½ pt. of water and half a teaspoonful of citric acid, bring to the boil and simmer for 20 minutes. The liquid turns a pale straw colour. Remove from the heat and carefully add a further ½ pt. of water. This will now be two pints of liquid containing 2 lbs. of invert sugar. If adding to wine in 2 oz. stages, 5 tablespoons of syrup equal approximately 2 ozs.

Once the first stage fermentation is completed, commence with the second stage (aerobic fermentation), by placing in fermentation vessel under airlock. This deprives the yeast of oxygen from the air, so that it turns entirely to conversion of sugar for oxygen by enzyme action. The progress can be monitored by the use of the hydrometer as described and the fermentation process halted when an s.g. of 1.00 is reached.

Post Fermentation

Once the fermentation has reached the required gravity indicated by the hydro-meter, the fermentation process is halted and the wine stabilised by adding 5 Campden tablets to the five gallon batch. Finings such as Bentonite are also added to clear the wine. Once the wine has cleared, usually in two to three days, it is then filtered off the lees into a storage vessel. To prevent secondary fermenta-tion some commercial wine makers add potassium sorbate (food standard E 202). In practice I have never experienced a malo-lactic* ferment, except in the rare circumstances when I have deliberately set out to induce a secondary fermenta-tion to impart special characteristics to a particular batch of wine.

It is at this stage that the balance of wine can be adjusted or indeed blended with another wine to adjust over-sweetness or acidity. It is best done by trial and error to suit one's own palate, but proceed with caution adding only small quantities of additives at a time.

To accelerate the process of maturation and to improve the bouquet of a young wine, lactic acid may be added. Normally it takes anything up to two years for the formation of lactic acid to develop in a maturing wine, but this can now be achieved in seconds by adding a few drops at a time until the desired result is obtained. The other complex esters will however not be present, and would be too complex an operation to be viable even for a commercial Vintner.

---

*A malo-lactic ferment is caused by the bacterium *Bacillus gracile* which converts the malic acid in the wine into lactic acid. This reaction produces gas and can be exploited to create a sparkling wine. This technique is often used by winemakers in Germany, Austria and Switzerland.

A malo-lactic ferment can produce a wine which is apparently sweeter than the original liquor prior to the secondary fermentation.

Bottling and Presentation

The wine is best matured in bulk and should be stored in an area free from direct light and large fluctuations in temperature. After a period of three to six months of maturing in bulk the wine can be tasted and any final adjustments carried out. If the wine appears too dry or acidic it may help to add some invert sugar syrup, the preparation of which is described on page 27. Alternatively an oversweet wine may be adjusted by blending with a dry wine of similar type.

Red wines are best bottled in brown or green glass, whilst white or rosé may be bottled in clear glass bottles.

The reason for using coloured glass for the bottling of red wine is because the red pigmentation or colouring matter may settle out as a deposit after being thrown out by the action of ultra-violet light. The red colouring agent may also be fugitive and will therefore fade in daylight.

Good presentation is of the utmost importance and should invite the tasting of its contents.

Wine should be racked into appropriate bottles according to type, that is, sparkling wines should always be in champagne bottles, a hock has a long tall brown bottle, while a moselle has the same shape but is green in colour.

If in doubt as to the appropriate bottle for the particular wine type, a trip to the local wine merchant will soon reveal the correct style for your batch to be bottled.

Fortifying

Needless controversy rages between many writers on the art of producing wine as to whether brandy or Polish spirit should be used to fortify. This is obviously because the authors have become proficient in the art without gaining an understanding of the chemical nature of the process. The answer is quite simple, if you wish to fortify a country wine then spirit such as Polish vodka is added as it is high in alcohol content and lacks flavour. Because it lacks flavour it will not destroy the delicate bouquet of the wine. If fortifying port or sherry type wine, then just as the commercial producers, brandy is used. If producing a liqueur then the appropriate corresponding spirit is used e.g. whisky for Drambuie type.

Port is made by stopping the fermentation before it is completed and then bringing the alcohol content up to the required strength by the addition of grape brandy.

The grape brandy referred to is produced from the residues of the initial wine making. The skins, pips, and other mucilage left over after the wine has been drawn off is added to water and a new fermentation started. The resulting poor quality wine produced is then put through a distillation process to produce the brandy used in the fortification.

Because of 'the stopping off' of the fermentation process in the making of port it explains its unique bouquet and flavour, and also why it is such a robust full bodied wine.

Having bottled the wine after any necessary adjustments, label and add foils as directed. Information concerning the making and date of bottling should be added to the wine label before laying down.

Before consumption the wine should be allowed a period of at least two months to 'recover'. During the recovery period the wine uses up absorbed air and builds up bouquet. The period of two months mentioned is the absolute minimum. At least six months to a year is recommended.

Recipes

Apple Wine

20 lbs. apples
3 lbs. sultanas
6 lbs. sugar approx. (use hydrometer)
2 tspns. citric acid
2 tspns. tartaric acid
1 tspn. pectic enzyme
Wine yeast
Bentonite

White grape juice (one pint) can be substituted for the sultanas if preferred.

Method:

Rinse apples in cold water. Core and quarter. Discard cores. Slice or mince, place in preparation vessel and cover with water to prevent browning. A sterilized plate can be used to hold pulp below surface of the water. Add sultanas after rinsing them in warm water. Dissolve acids and tannin in luke warm water (cooled from boiling), and add to prepared vessel. Dissolve sugar in water and add. Check gravity and adjust according to required alcohol content and preferred wine type (refer to chart on pages 52 and 53).

Add pectic enzyme, then switch on heater. When temperature reaches 65 degrees F. add yeast. After seven days or when violent fermentation slows, transfer to fermentation vessel under airlock. Allow to ferment to an s.g. of 1.00 then add three Campden tablets and Bentonite.

Wine should be crystal clear in approximately three days.

Rack off into storage vessel. Adjustments can be made at this stage but it is best to let the wine settle for a few months.

N.B. Malic acid is not included in this recipe for apple wine, as there is already a high concentration of this acid present in the fruit. It is advisable to aim for a balance of acids whenever possible.

Recommended yeast (if not using all purpose): Sparkling-champagne; sweet–sauternes type.

Apple

Contains: Vitamins, E, B17
Minerals, calcium, magnesium phosphorous.
If pectin retained – will lower cholesterol levels.

Medicinal Uses

Apple wine is a general tonic on its own as are most country wines. In ancient times it was used as a cure all mentioned by Galen in the 2nd century.

For specific complaints try these recipes.

Halitosis

Soak a sprig of dill and rosemary in a cupful of apple wine for seven days. Keep covered and out of daylight. Decant into a dark bottle with stopper.

Rinse the mouth with the lotion after cleaning teeth first thing in the morning for day long freshness.

Chilblains

Prepare infusion as above using the herbs angelica, lady's mantle, rosemary, sage, mint (apple or peppermint).

Wash feet then gently massage lotion onto affected areas. If area to be treated is sore and painful to the touch then apply with pads of cotton wool.

Lotion is rapidly absorbed by the skin so keep adding to avoid area becoming dry. Continue treatment until all irritation has ceased. Repeat treatment morning and evening until all signs of chilblains have gone.

My wife used to suffer agonies with this complaint, with loss of sleep due to irritation and severe swelling of toes. Despite using a proprietary cream and taking a course of tablets the relief from this complaint was minimal.

Having become interested to discover whether there was any substance in the claims made by herbalists, I prepared a lotion similar to the one described above, and after much persuasion it was applied to the affected area. Initially I suspect merely to humour me, and as it was prepared with a wine base which had previously been drunk with much enthusiasm, could do no harm. Despite having a highly sceptical 'patient' it is hard to know who was most surprised to learn that after only two applications the irritation was relieved and in less than a week all symptoms ceased. It was all the more surprising that it worked so rapidly, as all the books I had read on herbs and herbalism indicated that treatment had to be carried out for much longer periods than commercial medicines for them to be effective. I surmised that perhaps the wine base had also contributed to the treatment. The alcohol content was obviously a potent disinfectant, but could not account for the cure. Research into the constituents employed revealed that konakian or vitamin K was present in the herbs and is often prescribed for chilblain sufferers. Apple contains vitamin E which accelerates the repair of tissue damage caused by burns. It was also interesting to discover that yeast contained three compounds classed in the vitamin B complex: folic acid, aminobenzic acid, and inositol, which are known to promote healthy skin. If these are indeed the active ingredients affecting the cure, then the wine was not only employing the alcohol content to leach out the active oils in the herbs, but was also combating their breakdown perhaps together with vitamin E as an antioxidant, and in addition was contributing additional beneficial vitamins from the yeast.

I am aware that the evidence would require far more research than I am capable of in both resources and time, but I believe 'circumstantial' as it is, the coincidences are too great to ignore. In any case there is substantial evidence of the practical kind to prove the usefulness of this lotion.

At a later date I was interested to read an article concerning the research into vitamin treatments for various skin conditions in which vitamin E was mentioned.

I have given quantities of this lotion to many people who have complained of suffering from chilblains and all have responded positively to the treatment.

Several friends impressed with the effectiveness of the lotion have suggested that I keep the information secret and start to manufacture on a commercial basis. I am opposed to this as it would defeat the objective of bringing to the attention of (I hope) a great many people the simplicity of self help and would make me part of the dependency syndrome that the large manufacturers have engineered. The benefits of self help for minor ailments, apart from the personal satisfaction, is that doctors and medical practitioners would have more time and resources to treat chronic illnesses and there would be huge savings to the economy if only a small proportion of medicines were made at home.

I have no doubt that the large drug companies have already considered this possibility and are at this very moment lobbying the Euro M.P.s to pass a law forbidding us from administering our own home cures, unless drunk as a wine.

It is worth mentioning that this winter my wife mentioned that her chilblains were starting to irritate once again.

The following day I offered to make her some fresh lotion as the one she had was now some six years old and I assumed the potency would have worn off after such a long period.

I was surprised to learn that she had already used the 'old' lotion and it had worked. It will be interesting to see whether it is effective in another six years.

Apricot Wine

12 lbs. apricots (stones removed)
10 lbs. sugar
4 lbs. sultanas (optional)
2 tspns. tartaric acid
2 tspns. citric acid
pectic enzyme
yeast nutrient
wine yeast
Bentonite

Method:

Proceed as for apple wine. This wine improves with age and is excellent after a year's storage.

Recommended yeast if not using all purpose: dry–chablis sweet–sauterne.

Barley Wine

8 lbs. pearl barley
8 lbs. sugar
5 lbs. raisins
3 tspns. citric acid
2 tspns. malic acid
1 tspn. tartaric acid
1 tspn. grape tannin
1 tspn. yeast nutrient
Wine yeast
Bentonite

Method:

Place barley in preparation vessel. Add raisins after rinsing in warm water (water cooled from boiling).

Dissolve sugar in warm water together with acids, nutrient, tannin, and yeast. Place in preparation vessel.

After seven days transfer to fermentation vessel discarding solids. Make up to five gallon mark with water.

When required s.g. is reached add four crushed Campden tablets, and one teaspoonful of Bentonite. Wine should be crystal clear after three days and ready to transfer to storage vessel. Use all purpose yeast with this recipe.

Barley Wine

Is a proven tonic for people convalescing after liver and kidney complaints or jaundice. One third of a sherry glass measure consumed first thing in the morning, followed by a glass of water and at least a half-hour before eating is the prescribed dosage. For adjuvants to increase potency of this tonic refer to section on herbs.

An ointment for the treatment of bruises and sprains can be prepared from this wine, together with a massage lotion for the relief of aching limbs.

To one pint of wine, soak a handful of comfrey and one of thyme for one week. Gentle warming of ingredients over a stove can make a lotion of lesser strength if required for immediate use. Decanted from the solids, half the liquor can be used to prepare an ointment as detailed in the herb section; the remaining portion can be used for a massage oil for the relief of aching limbs. To the massage oil it is advisable to add a quantity of glycerine to provide body and reduce rate of evaporation. It has since been discovered that glycerine is absorbed by the skin and the beneficial ingredients are absorbed along with it. It is also hygroscopic (water absorbent) so can re-introduce a balance of liquid to cells in the epidermis. At the same time, by allowing the passage of alcohol, dissolved in the mixture, grime and fatty substances blocking the sebaceous and sweat glands are cleared thus creating a healthier moist skin.

Anti-ageing Lotion and Cream

Ladies who wish to look ten years younger should try this anti-ageing lotion which can also be incorporated as a cream (see herb section for details on cream preparation).

1 part comfrey root, 1 part nettle leaves (young), 1 part marigold, 1 part evening primrose, 1 part lady's mantle.

Cover with wine in a dark vessel and allow to soak for ten days. Decant lotion from solids and store in a dark well stoppered vessel. If using as a lotion then add glycerine obtainable from any chemist for the reasons described above.

Comfrey Root

Contains allantoin and other compounds which promote healthy cell growth. Plus orotic acid, said to prevent premature ageing.

Marigold

Has antiseptic and anti-inflammatory properties. (Flowers are preferable but the plant can be used as well).

Evening Primrose

Contains gamma linoleic acid which the body uses to build healthy cell structures and produce prosta glandins together with other compounds for maintaining healthy skin.

Lady's Mantle

Acts as a regulator on the growth of epitherial tissues.

If being used for the treatment of ageing skin and the removal of age spots it can be mixed with the carrot and apple remedy described earlier.

When preparing wine for these remedies then natural ingredients should be used.

Beetroot Wine

15 lbs. beetroot
4 lbs. raisins
10 lbs. sugar approx.
1 tspn. grape tannin
1 tspn. tartaric acid
2 tspns. malic acid
1 tspn. citric acid
1 tspn. yeast nutrient
1 tspn. Bentonite
Wine yeast. (Port type
or general purpose)

Method:

Scrub and dice beetroot and place in preparation vessel. Add raisins after rinsing in warm water. Raisins (dried black grapes) give extra flavour, body and smoothness to the wine and help nourish the yeast. Proceed as for blackberry wine.

Beetroot Wine

Is an excellent blood purifier. A diuretic – Carminative–Depurative. Also useful for combating excessive flatulence when diluted with equal parts of clean cold water.

Dosage – one cupful morning after breakfast and one cup after evening meal.

N.B. Wine should not be consumed at any other time of the day with or without food as this will negate the beneficial properties of the treatment.

As a medicine for coughs or bronchial disorders add equal parts of honey and take whenever condition warrants.

Effectiveness may be improved by the addition of herbs listed in herb section.

Blackcurrant Wine

15 lbs. blackcurrants
4 lbs. raisins
10 lbs. sugar approx.
1 tspn. pectic enzyme
1 tspn. yeast nutrient
Wine yeast – Port type

Proceed as for blackberry wine.

Blackcurrant Wine

Because of the high content of vitamin C in blackcurrants this wine can be used as a general tonic and in the treatment of complaints listed under ascorbic acid in the vitamins section.

For a specific complaint refer to adjuvants in herb section.

Blackberry Wine

20 lbs. blackberries
3 lbs. raisins (optional)
10 lbs. sugar
1 tspn. grape tannin
1 tspn. tartaric acid
2 tspn. malic acid
1 tspn. citric acid
1 tspn. yeast nutrient
Wine yeast – Port type
1 tspn. pectic enzyme

Method:

Mash blackberries in water, and add raisins after they have been rinsed in warm water (cooled from boiling). Add remainder of ingredients after dissolving them in warm water.

Dissolve other ingredients and add to bulk. Make up to mark.

Check s.g. with hydrometer and adjust as necessary.

After seven to ten days fermentation will become less vigorous and it should then be transferred to fermentation vessel under airlock. Maintain temperature at 70° Fahrenheit. When s.g. reaches 1.00, add four Campden tablets and Bentonite. Wine should be crystal clear within seven days.

Transfer to storage vessel.

Blackberry Wine

Useful with adjuvants or on its own for bronchial and respiratory complaints with good expectorant properties.

Is useful as a blood cleanser and general tonic for convalescents.

Especially useful as an anti-toxin provided it is under strict medical supervision.

Those suffering from asthmatic attacks may find this wine beneficial if taken immediately at the onset of the symptoms.

Blueberry Wine

1 gallon of blueberries
5 lbs raisins
10 lbs sugar
2 tspns. citric acid
2 tspns. malic acid
1 tspn. tartaric acid
1 tspn. pectic enzyme
2 tspns. yeast nutrient
Wine yeast
1 tspn. Bentonite

Proceed as for blackberry wine.

Blueberry Wine

High in vitamins and minerals, this is undoubtedly a prince of beneficial wines. Although the fruit is relatively expensive compared to other wine ingredients it is well worth the making. Furthermore, from one batch of fruit three batches of wine can be made. The first, a rich port type wine, decant liquor and to the solids *start again and treat as fresh fruit*, this will produce a full bodied red wine. Repeat process to produce a lighter more delicate table wine.

As the cost of the fruit is high, ensure that you purchase only the best organic grown fruit direct from a reputable producer. Old fruit on supermarket shelves will have lost a considerable amount of goodness and will produce a disappointing, inferior wine.

I am lucky in living close to Trehane's Nursery in Longham near Wimborne, Dorset, where blueberries of excellent quality can be purchased. The owners, despite being very busy are always pleased to give advice on making wine from their fruit. If you are making a large quantity of wine and are prepared to spend some time doing your own picking then you can probably negotiate a special price for a larger amount.

It is astringent and antiseptic and is ideal as a mouth wash for gum boils or soreness caused by dentures, and as a respiratory aid with a catarrhal cold.

It is also claimed to be a good blood cleanser and reduce cholesterol levels, but I can find no evidence from the constituents of the berry, nor any written cases recorded, so I am doubtful about the latter properties.

Broccoli Wine

1 gallon broccoli tops and leaves

Remainder of ingredients and quantities as for clover wine (If purple broccoli is used a nice rose wine is achieved.)

Bullace Wine

20 lbs. bullaces
4 lbs. raisins
10 lbs. sugar approx.
1 tspn. pectic enzyme
2 tspns. yeast nutrient
Wine yeast

Remove stones from fruit, then proceed as for blackberry.

Carrot Wine

20 lbs. carrots
4 lbs. raisins
10 lbs. sugar
2 tspn. grape tannin
2 tspn. malic acid
2 tspn. citric acid
2 tspn. yeast nutrient
Wine yeast

Method:

Scrub and dice carrots. Add raisins after rinsing in warm water. Add other ingredients after dissolving in water. Make up to mark and adjust s.g. to required level.

After initial fermentation subsides (usually 10 days), transfer to fermentation vessel under airlock. When s.g. reaches 1.00, add 4 crushed Campden tablets plus Bentonite.

Wine should be crystal clear within six days when it can be transferred to storage vessel.

Carrot wine is a very old country medicine said to have beneficial curative properties and to be a restorative tonic during convalescence.

Carrot Wine

Another very old country remedy, how old is hard to determine. Certainly since records have been kept, but obviously not in this country until the fifteenth century, when they were introduced from Holland. It is interesting to note that there were two carrots, the purple and white, as the orange carrot had not been cultivated up to this time. The purple carrot produced a mutant yellow variety that was selectively bred as a separate variety by the Dutch.

Later in the seventeenth century an orange mutant appeared which was then selectively bred and presumably because of its pleasing appearance completely replaced the earlier varieties.

Effective for complaints of the gastro-intestinal organs, and combating flatulence and stomach acidity due to nervous tension. A good tonic when suffering from exhaustion and tired eyes. The potassium salts account for the diuretic properties of the plant. Also contains an agent that is effective against roundworm.

It is said to promote the onset of menstruation but I have been unable to find any medical evidence to support this claim with my limited time for research.

Celery Wine

20 lbs. celery
4 lbs. sultanas
2 tspns. grape tannin
2 tspns. citric acid
1 tspn. malic acid
1 tspn. tartaric acid
2 tspns. yeast nutrient
10 lbs. sugar (check hydrometer)
Wine yeast – general purpose

Method:

Wash celery then chop into small chunks. Place in preparation vessel. Proceed as in recipe for carrot wine using pulp fermentation.

Celery Wine

Is a strong diuretic and is not recommended when kidney problems are diagnosed unless under strict medical supervision. Taken internally this wine is said to help with external skin problems.

As an aphrodisiac include the root of celery when making the wine. An essential oil in the root is used to restore sexual potency previously reduced by stress or illness. For an explosive mixture mix with apple and barley wine (see vitamin E).

The author accepts no liability whatsoever for those persons trying this mixture.

Cherry Wine

Quantities as for celery wine. Remove stones from fruit then proceed as in recipe for carrot wine with the addition of pectic enzyme using pulp fermentation.

Clover Wine

5 gallons of clover blossoms
3 lbs. sultanas
2 tspns. grape tannin
2 tspns. citric acid
2 tspns. malic acid
1 tspn. tartaric acid
10 lbs. sugar approx.
2 tspns. yeast nutrient
Wine yeast – general purpose
or sauternes type

Method:

Dissolve sugar and other ingredients in water which has cooled from boiling. When cold, pour on clover blossoms which have already been rinsed in clean water.

Switch on heater and when temperature reaches 65° Fahrenheit, add wine yeast. preparation vessel with the dried fruit. Discard remainder of the stones. Add mark. Vigorous fermentation should have slowed after a period of seven days when the must should be transferred to the fermentation vessel under airlock. When desired s.g. is reached add five Campden tablets and Bentonite. Wine should be clear within five days and ready to transfer to storage vessel.

This wine should be ready for drinking after ten months in storage.

Clover Wine

Stimulates liver and gall bladder activity. Ideal for restoring appetite in convalescents.

Massage on to feet to combat foot odour and athlete's foot.

39

Coltsfoot Wine

10 lbs. sugar – check s.g.
2 gallons of coltsfoot flowers
3 lbs. sultanas
2 tspns. grape tannin
3 tspsn. citric acid
2 tspns. malic acid
1 tspn. tartric acid
2 tspns. yeast nutrient
2 tspns. Bentonite
Wine yeast

Proceed as for clover wine.

Coltsfoot Wine

An ancient recipe for the treatment of coughs, colds and bronchial complaints in general. It is a demulcent, emollient and expectorant. Externally it can be used for the treatment of insect bites, inflammation of the skin, leg ulcers and Phlebitis.

Cowslip Wine

Cowslips growing in the wild are protected by law. You can however grow your own, as I do.

One packet of seeds will produce many plants which will multiply rapidly over the years.

Quantities of ingredients as for coltsfoot wine. Proceed as for clover wine.

Cowslip Wine

Many people are allergic to the essential ingredients contained in the primula family and should therefore avoid these medications. Test a small quantity for allergic reaction before commencing on a course of treatment.

Cowslips properties are said to be: Anodyne, Diuretic and expectorant. They are used in the treatment of general nervous conditions, migraine headaches and insomnia. The excellent expectorant is useful for clearing cattarrh and mucous congestion. It also said to have anti wrinkling effect on the skin, so could be added to beauty preparations.

Crab Apple Wine

Recipe as for apple wine.

Cranberry Wine

1 gallon of cranberries
5 lbs raisins
10 lbs sugar
2 tspns. citric acid
2 tspns. malic acid
1 tspn. tartaric acid
1 tspn. pectic enzyme
2 tspns. yeast nutrient
Wine yeast
1 tspn. Bentonite

Proceed as for blackberry wine.

Cranberry Wine and Cherry Wine

Has no specific medicinal attributes other than a general tonic.

Damson Wine

12 lbs. damsons
3 lbs. raisins
10 lbs. sugar approx
2 tspns. citric acid
1 tspn. tartaric acid
1 tspn. pectic enzyme
2 tspns. yeast nutrient
1 tspn. Bentonite
Wine yeast

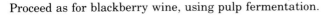

Proceed as for blackberry wine, using pulp fermentation.

Damson Wine

An aperient, astringent, diaphoretic, diuretic, stomachic.
   Is ideal as a mild laxative.
   Gargle with damson wine for inflamation of the mouth and throat. However excellent the vintage may be, do not be tempted to swallow afterwards.

41

Dandelion Wine

2 gallons of dandelion heads
3 lbs. sultanas
10 lbs. sugar approx.
3 tspns. citric acid
2 tspns. malic acid
1 tspn. tartaric acid
1 tspn. grape tannin
2 tspns. yeast nutrient
Wine yeast

Method:

Discard all pieces of green leaf or stalk as they will make the wine bitter. Wash flowers in water then gently press into measuring jug to obtain correct quantity. Place in preparation vessel together with sultanas that have previously been rinsed in warm water. Dissolve sugar, acids, nutrient, tannin, and add to preparation vessel. Adjust water level and s.g. Allow vigorous fermentation for seven days at 70° Fahrenheit. If fermentation slows in the first four days, 'rouse wine' by stirring with a beating action. Transfer to fermentation vessel, and ferment on to an s.g. of 1.00, under airlock. Add four crushed Campden tablets and Bentonite to clarify and stabilize the wine.

After four days wine should be crystal clear and a bright golden colour. Transfer to storage vessel. If acidic adjustment required, add a teaspoonful of lactic acid to see if this improves wine. Allow wine to mature for at least six months before attempting any further adjustments.

Dandelion Wine

An ancient wine medicine that is so highly regarded as a country beverage that the beneficial medicinal properties have been largely forgotten.

Is a source of the Vitamins A, B, C, E & K.

A cholagogue, aperient, stomachic, diuretic.

By the promotion of bile aids stimulation of appetite.

Helps body to secrete toxins and body fluids.

Is said to be beneficial as a mild laxative, for treatment of dyspepsia, insomnia, jaundice and other liver problems.

Date Wine   The favourite drink of the harem?

15 lbs. dried dates
2 lbs. sultanas
10 lbs. sugar approx
4 tspns. citric acid
2 tspns. malic acid
1 tspn. pectic enzyme
1 tspn. yeast nutrient
Wine yeast
(Port or sherry type)

Method:

Remove stones from dates but add approximately a quarter of them to the preparation vessel with the dried fruit. Discard remainder of the stones. Add sultanas after rinsing. Dissolve remainder of ingredients in water and add. Make up to the mark with cooled previously boiled water. Violent frothing occurs in the first four days. If fermentation appears less vigorous than expected then rouse the wine. This will increase the oxygen level by beating air into the must which assists the yeast to multiply.

Once vigorous fermentation has slowed transfer to fermentation vessel under airlock, and ferment on until an s.g. of 1.00 is reached. Do not allow fermentation to continue beyond this point. Add five Campden tablets and Bentonite. After four days wine should be clear, and ready to rack from lees into storage vessel, prior to bottling or blending. To a wine glass of the batch add a drop or two of lactic acid, if this appears to improve the taste and bouquet, then add one teaspoonful to the bulk in the storage container.

Date Wine

Is a good basis for skin lotions or creams with herbal additions, or may be added to wine with a low vitamin B2 and B3 content as a supplement to a tonic.

Elderberry Wine (Traditional)

2 gallons elderberries
3 ozs. bruised root ginger (optional)
10 lbs. sugar approx.
2 tspns. citric acid
3 tspns. malic acid
1 tspn. tartaric acid
1 tspn. pectic enzyme
1 tspn. yeast nutrient
Wine yeast (port type)

Method:

Place elderberries in preparation vessel after stripping them from their stalks with a fork. Cover with water to which two Campden tablets have been added. Dissolve all ingredients except yeast in water and add. When must reaches a temperature of 65° Fahrenheit, add port wine yeast and stir well. When initial fermentation has subsided, usually within seven days, transfer must to fermentation vessel. Check s.g. at regular intervals and when a reading of 1.00 is obtained add four Campden tablets and Bentonite to stabilize and clarify. Transfer to storage vessel. The wine is delicious whilst young but improves greatly with keeping. Some of the very old recipes included a dozen cloves, which can be added if desired.

Elderberry Wine

Has been a favourite country brew for centuries. It is widely known to be a cold weather tonic able to combat the onslaught of colds and flu.

It is used as a Cathartic, Diaphoretic, Diuretic, purgative and stimulant. At the first sign of a cold or flu a sherry glassful taken before retiring will work wonders. It will ease mucous congestion, reduce the symptoms of headache due to colds and rheumatic pains and is said to stimulate and induce sweating.

Caution To some people the purgative action is extreme so do not be tempted to double up on the dosage unless familiar with the effects. The action of this wine is mildly laxative so is ideal for the treatment of mild constipation.

Elderberry Port

Elderberries were once added to port wine made in Portugal to improve flavour and colour, until legislation halted the practice. This practice tells us quite a lot about the qualities of the elderberry.

This ancient wine recipe produces one of the noblest country wines. A rich robust wine full of body and flavour comparable to a very expensive commercially produced product. Despite the quality it is very cheap to make if the berries are collected for free from a country hedgerow or river bank. Be careful to avoid hedegrows polluted by traffic or farmland where crops have been sprayed.

The variety of the berry and the acidity of the soil in which it is growing can affect the characteristics of the berry and the flavour of the wine produced from it.

I collect mine each year from a bank beside a flowing stream and the fruits are consistantly good whatever the climate.

3 gallons of elderberries
15 lbs. sugar
3 lbs. raisins
2 lbs. bananas
2 tspns. malic acid
1 tspn. citric acid
1 tspn. tartaric acid
2 tspns. yeast nutrient
Port wine yeast

N.B. This recipe requires no addition of tannin due to the high content of this ingredient in the berry.

Method:

Cover the elderberries in the preparation vessel with cold water. Add raisins after rinsing in warm water. Chop bananas into small pieces and add. Dissolve other ingredients in water and add to bulk, apart from wine yeast. Apply heat, and when temperature reaches 70° Fahrenheit, add wine yeast.

When vigorous fermentation has slowed, transfer must to preparation vessel dispensing with all solid residue.

When s.g. reaches 1.00, add four crushed Campden tablets and Bentonite. Wine should be clear within five days and ready to transfer to storage vessel. Fortify with brandy according to table on pages 52 and 53.

The longer this wine is kept the more it improves. It is a characteristic of such a deep red full-bodied wine, to throw a deposit while ageing. It is a good idea therefore to hold in bulk before bottling for as long as is practical. Do not be disappointed if wine has thrown a deposit even after several rackings, as all the best old vintage ports have this characteristic. Hence the ceremonial decanting of fine and rare ports before consumption.

Elderflower Wine

A light fragrant wine, which can form the basis for a champagne.

½ gallon of elderflowers
10 lbs. sugar
2 lbs sultanas
2 tspns. citric acid
2 tspns. malic acid
2 tspns. tartaric acid
1 tspn. grape tannin
2 tspns. yeast nutrient
Champagne yeast

Method:

Rinse blooms in water, cooled from boiling. Dissolve soluble ingredients in warm water then add all other ingredients except yeast: pour over flower heads, add 4 Campden tablets and allow to stand for 48 hours. When the temperature is above 60° F add yeast. After vigorous fermentation subsides decant into fermentation vessel, add-air lock and proceed as for clover wine.

Elderflower Wine

Diaphoretic, Vasodilator, Demulcent. Elderflower wine is useful as an antiseptic wash for skin inflammation and treatment of boils. It has a mild diuretic properties and is claimed to be useful in the treatment of rheumatic pains and gout.

Elderflower Champagne

To produce a sparkling wine follow the process for elderflower but fine the wine with Bentonite just before gravity reaches 1.010. As soon as wine is clear, bottle in champagne bottles. Make sure corks are well rammed down. Allow fermentation to continue for a further four weeks, gradually inverting the bottles and giving them a sharp twist each day. Residual yeast should then be lying on cork.

Prepare a freezing mixture by mixing two ounces of salt with one pint of ice. Place neck of bottle in freezing mixture for ten minutes. When carrying out operations with sparkling wine it is wise to take certain precautions, as there can be considerable pressure built up in the bottle. Wrap bottle in an old towel and always ensure that cork is pointing away from you or any one else in the vicinity.

Remove bottle from freezing mixture and carefully remove cork with dead yeast and lees frozen to it. Quickly replace with champagne stoppers. Wire down, label and add champagne foils. Do not prime the bottles with a spoonful of sugar as advised in some books, there is sufficient uncoverted sugar in the wine providing the hydrometer readings have been taken correctly. The addition of extra sugar, apart from being a hit and miss affair, may well result in bottles exploding or the wine merely being a burst of foam. Good champagne should not have an excess of froth, but should give a steady stream of carbon dioxide bubbles over an extended period of time. It should not fizz like lemonade then lie flat within moments of pouring. The bottles should not be shaken before opening, like all wines it should be handled delicately and with due respect in keeping with its character.

Fig Wine Full of Mediterranean Promise?

8 lbs. of figs
2 lbs. sultanas
10 lbs. sugar approx.
4 tspns. citric acid
2 tspns. malic acid
1 tspn. tartaric acid
1 tspn. pectic enzyme
1 tspn. yeast nutrient
1 tspn. Bentonite
Wine yeast

Method:

Place figs in preparation vessel after dicing, and cover. Dissolve sugar and other ingredients in water apart from wine yeast and add to preparation vessel. Make up to the mark with water adjusting the s.g. as necessary. Switch on heater, and when temperature reaches 65° F. add yeast. When first vigorous fermentation has died down, transfer bulk to fermentation vessel under airlock. Discard residual solids. When correct s.g. has been reached add four Campden tablets and Bentonite. As soon as wine has cleared transfer to storage vessel.

The acidic balance may need adjusting with a small amount of lactic acid.

Fig wine acts as a demulcent, laxative and emollient. Mix with equal parts of honey to make a demulcent to soothe mucous membranes for coughs, colds and flu.

Ginger Wine

A strong warming wine ideal for cold winter evenings.

4 lbs. root ginger
2 lbs. sultanas
10 lbs. sugar
4 tspns. citric acid
2 tspns. malic acid
2 tspns. tartaric acid
1 tspn. yeast nutrient
1 tspn. Bentonite
Wine yeast

Method:

Wrap ginger in clean tea towel and crush with rolling pin. Place in preparation vessel and add sultanas. Dissolve all ingredients except yeast in water and add to bulk. Make up to mark with water, adjusting s.g. as required. When temperature reaches 65–70° F. add yeast and ferment on to a hydrometer reading of 1.00. Add four Campden tablets and Bentonite. As soon as wine has cleared transfer to storage vessel.

Ginger wine is an appetizer-carminative, diaphoretic, sialogogue. Promotes perspiration and is said to be useful for colic and pains of the stomach caused by indigestion or flatulence.

Golden Rod Wine

4 pints golden rod flowers
3 lbs. raisins
10 lbs. sugar (check s.g.)
4 tspns. citric acid
4 tspns. malic acid
1 tspn. tartaric acid
2 tspns. yeast nutrient
1 tspn. Bentonite
Wine yeast

Proceed as for clover wine.

(Solidago) – from the latin solidaris (to make whole), refers to early healing properties of the herb.

Golden Rod Wine

Is an appetizer, an astringent, a carminative, a diaphoretic, and a stimulant. It is used as a tonic for invalids who have lost their appetite. It is said that the American Indians applied a lotion made from the flowers of this plant to bee stings and insect bites.

It is an excellent medicine for the treatment of fresh wounds, ulcerated gums and boils. Culpepper claimed that 'a decoction is serviceable to fasten the teeth when loose'. I presume that he is not talking about dentures.

Gooseberry Wine 'The hairy grape'

So called as, like the grape, the gooseberry has a good balance of natural acids and nutrients.

The sugar extraction method works well with this fruit. By stopping the fermentation at a gravity of 1.010 and proceeding as for a sparkling wine (see Elderflower Champagne), a light refreshing wine with a brilliant sparkle is produced.

15 lbs. gooseberries
10 lbs. sugar
4 lbs. sultanas
1 tspn. pectic enzyme
1 tspn. yeast nutrient
1 tspn. Bentonite
Wine yeast (sauternes
or champagne type)
1tspn. citric acid
1 tspn. tartaric acid

Use one of the methods to extract juice, as described in the section, under 'preparation of must', and proceed as for blackberry wine.

Gooseberry Wine

Over the centuries there have been a considerable amount of claims made for the beneficial medical properties of gooseberries one of which is Euphoriant which I dismissed as there appeared to be no chemical constituent that could support this.

A very good friend of mine however used to produce gooseberry wine commercially under the name of 'PRISTINA'. The wine was produced sweet, semi-sweet or dry. In my opinion, and in the opinion of a great many local people, friends and relatives, this was one of the most delicious wines we had ever tasted. It was very sad therefore and a great disappointment to many that he was forced to close the winery due to the punitive taxes necessary to the Customs and Excise. Duty was payable even before the wine was bottled and sold. This white wine was made with frozen fruit which undoubtedly helped in releasing all the juices and at the same time preserved many of the beneficial ingredients. During a meal with my sister, and brother in law, in which we had only consumed part of a bottle we were all laughing until the tears streamed down our cheeks, we blamed the wine for our behaviour. At a later date some friends to whom we had given a bottle to try, stated that the wine must have been strong because all the dinner guests had been convulsed with laughter. We related our own experience to our friends and from then on the wine was known as 'Giggley Gooseberry'. It may therefore confirm the claim to be an euphoriant. Whatever the claims made it undoubtedly contains many vitamins and minerals and is beneficial to all if consumed in moderation.

I have not had a chance to make this wine with frozen fruit as all my produce to date has gone straight to the kitchen. Perhaps one day I shall have a bumper crop so that there is sufficient for at least one five gallon batch.

Gorse Flower Wine

4 pts. fresh gorse flowers
4 lbs. sultanas
10 lbs. sugar
1 tspn. citric acid
4 tspns. tartaric acid
1 tspn. malic acid
1 tspn. yeast nutrient
wine yeast

Proceed as for clover wine.

Gorse Flower Wine (Furze Wine)

Unlike much of the plant life of this country it is not of foreign origin, and is a primeavel member of the English flora. There is evidence that furze was harvested by stone age man so perhaps they were brewing even in those early days. It has been suggested however that it was gathered for animal feed, perhaps to entice some unsuspecting animal into the path of a heavy boulder perhaps?

Claimed by early physicians to be effective for the treatment of the liver, spleen, and the kidneys.

It was also prescribed by Culpepper for the treatment of jaundice.

Grape Wine

Quantities and method as for Gooseberry Wine but omit the sultanas.

Grape Vine Wine

½ gallon of vine shoots
4 lbs. sultanas
10 lbs. sugar
2 tspns. citric acid
1 tspn. yeast nutrient
Wine yeast
1 tspn. Bentonite
1 tspn. malic acid

Method:

Wash vine prunings, discarding any older woodier pieces. Place in preparation vessel together with sultanas that have previously been rinsed in warm water then sterilize must with 5 Campden tablets. Dissolve other ingredients in water and add. When temperature reaches 65° F. add yeast and continue as laid down in previous recipes.

Greengage Wine

16 lbs. greengages
10 lbs. sugar approx
2 lbs. sultanas
3 tspns. citric acid
2 tspns. tartaric acid
1 tspn. malic acid
1 tspn. grape tannin
1 tspn. pectic enzyme
1 tspn. yeast nutrient
Wine yeast

Proceed as for blackberry wine.

Hawthorn Blossom Wine

1½ gallons hawthorn blossoms
1 lbs. sultanas
10 lbs. sugar
2 tspns. citric acid
3 tspns. malic acid
2 tspns. tartaric acid
1 tspn. grape tannin
1 tspns. yeast nutrient
Wine yeast

Proceed as for clover wine.

Hawthorn Blossom Wine (May Blossom)

Anti-spasmodic – Sedative – Diuretic-Heart Stimulant. The ancients attributed many magical properties as well as medicinal uses to may blossom. It is woven into many old beliefs and superstitions not the least of course being the famous bush at Glastonbury that is said to flower each year on Christmas Day. Apothecaries used this herb in the treatment of pleurisy, vertigo, gout, insomnia and angina. Culpepper claimed that the berries of hawthorn beaten to a powder in a pestle and mortar and drunk in wine are a remedy for the stone and no less effectual for the dropsy.

Like the gorse the hawthorn was used by our prehistoric ancestors.

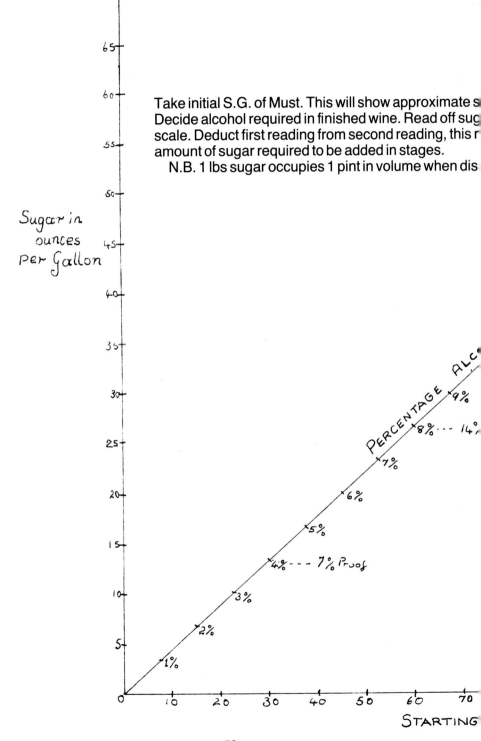

Take initial S.G. of Must. This will show approximate s
Decide alcohol required in finished wine. Read off sug
scale. Deduct first reading from second reading, this r
amount of sugar required to be added in stages.
 N.B. 1 lbs sugar occupies 1 pint in volume when dis

Sugar in
ounces
per Gallon

PERCENTAGE ALC

9%
8% --- 14°
7%
6%
5%
4% --- 7% Proof
3%
2%
1%

STARTING

52

tent.
n lower
ts the

n must.

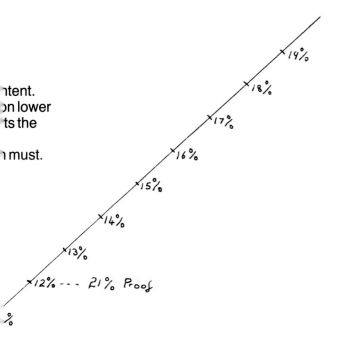

19%
18%
17%
16%
15%
14%
13%
12% --- 21% Proof
%

Reduce or increase Gravity reading by one for every 5° C below or
above 20° C.

      Starting Gravities: Dry wine   85–105
                      Medium wine 105–120
                      Sweet wine   120–150

N.B. Gravity = S.G. with decimal point omitted.

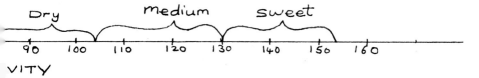

Dry   medium   sweet

90   100   110   120   130   140   150   160

VITY

Hop Wine

2 gallons of hop cones
2 lbs. sultanas
10 lbs. sugar
2 tspns. grape tannin
4 tspns. citric acid
2 tspns. malic acid
1 tspn. tartaric acid
1 tspn. yeast nutrient
1 tspn. Bentonite
Wine yeast

Method:

Discard any pieces of green leaf or stalk and gently press down in measuring jug to obtain correct volume. Lightly rinse blossoms in fresh water, and place in preparation vessel. Add sultanas after rinsing in warm water. Dissolve sugar and acids together with tannin and nutrients in water and adjust s.g. whilst making up to the mark. Switch on heat, and when temperature reaches 65° F. add wine yeast. When stage one fermentation has slowed (usually seven days), transfer to fermentation vessel under airlock. When desired s.g. is achieved, add five Campden tablets and Bentonite. After three to five days wine should be clear and ready to transfer to a storage container. Take a small wine glass full of the wine and add a few drops of lactic acid. If this improves wine to the palate, then add a teaspoonful to the bulk to hasten the maturation process.

Hop Wine

Anodyne – Diuretic – Febrifuge – Hypnotic – Sedative – Tonic.
    It is said to be a strong sedative and is therefore recommended for insomnia, nervous diarrhoea, and restlessness.

Lemon Wine

30 good size lemons
2 lbs. sultanas
10 lbs. sugar
2 tspns. malic acid
2 tspns. grape tannin
1 tspn. pectic enzyme
1 tspns. yeast nutrient
Wine yeast

Method:

Extract the juice from the lemons and add to preparation vessel together with sultanas that have previously been rinsed in warm water. Dissolve sugar, acids, grape tannin and yeast nutrient in water and add to bulk, together with pectic enzyme. When temperature reaches 65° F. add wine yeast. Make up to the mark and adjust s.g. as necessary.

Allow first vigorous fermentation to slow down before transferring to fermentation vessel. Allow fermentation to continue until an s.g. of 1.00 is achieved.

Add five Campden tablets and Bentonite and wine should clear within four days. Adjust as required and transfer to storage vessel.

Lemon Wine

Bactericide – vermifuge – febrifuge – anti-neuralgic.

Lemon is a popular home remedy for coughs and flu, and for this reason is often incorporated in pharmaceutical preparations. Citrus fruits are known to have a high concentration of Vitamin C which is known to be able to ward off the worst affects of the common cold.

For flu, or a persistent cough, sweeten lemon wine with honey and warm. Drink a hot glassful before retiring at night. If the cold is of a feverish nature then herbs may be added when warming the concoction to induce sweating and relieve the congestion of the nasal passages. (See diaphoretic and expectorant in herb section.)

Lime Blossom Wine

The blossoms from lime trees have a superb aroma and impart a unique flavour to this wine.

1½ gallons of lime blossoms
10 lbs. sugar
3 lbs. sultanas
4 tspns. citric acid
3 tspns. malic acid
2 tspns. tartaric acid
1 tspn. yeast nutrient
1 tspn. Bentonite
Wine yeast –
Sauternes or general purpose

Proceed as for other flower recipes.

Loganberry Wine

The sugar extraction method can be used for this wine. Ingredients and method as for blackberry wine.

Malt Wine

2 gallons of malt
2 ozs. bruised root ginger
2 lbs. sultanas
10 lbs. sugar approx.
3 tspns. citric acid
2 tspns. malic acid
2 tspns. tartaric acid
2 tspns. grape tannin
Wine yeast and Bentonite

Method:

Boil the malt and bruised ginger in water for thirty minutes, then add to preparation vessel when cool. Add 5 Campden tablets and dissolve.

Rinse sultanas in warm water and add to malt after draining. Dissolve sugar, acids, tannin, and yeast nutrient, then add to bulk followed by yeast nutrient.

When temperature reaches 65–70° F. add wine yeast. Ferment until vigorous fermentation slows and transfer to fermentation vessel under airlock. When desired s.g. is reached add five Campden tablets and Bentonite and allow to clear completely before transferring to storage vessel.

Marigold Wine

2 gallons of marigold blossoms
2 lbs. sultanas
10 lbs. sugar approx
4 tspns. citric acid
2 tspns. malic acid
1 tspn. tartaric acid
2 tspns. grape tannin
2 tspns. yeast nutrient
1 tspn. Bentonite
Wine yeast

Proceed as for clover wine.

Marigold Wine

Anti-spasmodic – aperient – cholagogue – diaphoretic – emmenagogue – sudorific.

Used internally for gastritis and menstrual problems and in the treatment for fevers and colitis.

It has been scientifically proven to be beneficial in the treatment of ulcerations of the mucosa of the stomach and bowel. Macerate a handful of the plant (both flowers and stalks may be used) in a cupful of wine. Repeat with an equal quantity of mint and wine. Decant both portions from the solids and stir gently to mix. The resultant mixture can be applied to bruises sprains, sores and boils. It is claimed that this mixture will also remove warts.

Culpepper stated 'the juice of marigold mixed with vinegar (or wine), and any hot swellings bathed with it, instantly giveth ease and assuageth it. The flowers either green or dried, are much used in possets, broths and drinks as a comforter of the heart and spirits and to expel any malignant or pestilential quality which might annoy them'.

The use of marigold to treat impetigo of the scalp was mentioned as early as the twelfth century in a medical journal.

Marrow Wine

2 large ripe marrows
3 lbs. sultanas
10 lbs. sugar
3 tspns. citric acid
2 tspns. malic acid
1 tspn. tartaric acid
2 tspns. grape tannin
1 tspn. pectic enzyme
1 tspn. yeast nutrient
1 tspn. Bentonite
Wine yeast

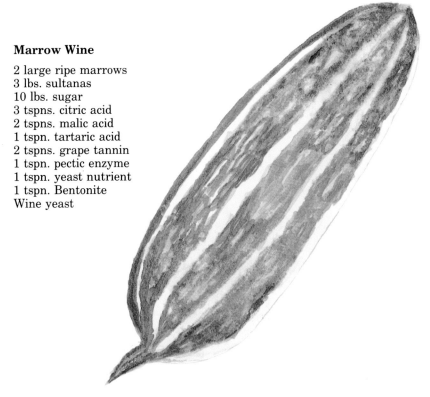

Method:

Cut marrows lengthways and scoop out pith and seeds. Discard pith and seeds and slice up remainder. Place in preparation vessel, then proceed as for blackberry wine.

Nettle Wine

Quantities and method as following recipe for oak leaf wine, substituting nettle leaves for oak leaves.
Always use fresh young nettle leaves.

Nettle Wine

Astringent – diuretic – galactogogue, haemostatic.
For centuries has been used for the treatment of rheumatic problems and ailments of the urinary tract. Claims have been made that it can promote milk flow in nursing mothers.
A decoction of the root in wine is recommended to halt the loss of hair.
Galen advised 'That the seeds of nettle taken in a draught of mulled wine will arouse desire'. This may explain in some part the old country belief that nettle seeds cured impotency and infertility in women.

Oak Leaf Wine

3 gallons of oak leaves
3 lbs. sultanas
10 lbs. sugar
3 tspns. citric acid
2 tspns. malic acid
2 tspns. tartaric acid
2 tspns. yeast nutrient
Wine yeast
1 tspn. Bentonite

The flavour and tannin content can be varied by picking the leaves at different times of the year.

Method:

Rinse leaves in cold water that has previously been boiled and allowed to cool, discarding any stalks or other foreign matter. Place in preparation vessel with sultanas. Dissolve sugar, acids, and yeast nutrient in water and add to bulk.
Make up to the mark with cool boiled water and switch on heater. When temperature reaches 65° F. add wine yeast.
Allow first stage fermentation to subside then transfer to fermentation vessel under airlock, being careful not to disturb sediment. Ferment to a s.g. of 1.00, then add four Campden tablets and Bentonite to stabilize and act as a preservative during maturation stages. When wine is clear check small quantity for acidity level. If low or wine seems lifeless add one drop at a time of lactic acid to the wine glass until the correct level is reached. For every drop of lactic acid required to the wine glassful, add one teaspoonful to the bulk, then transfer wine to storage vessel. Ensure that acid is stirred well into the batch. Allow to mature in bulk for at least six months before bottling.
Remember when adjusting wine that acidity or harshness of a newly fermented wine will reduce with age during the maturation stages. It is a good practice to take regular tastings of the must, and wine, during all the stages of making and maturation. Experience will then show what is needed to balance a wine.

Oak Leaf Wine

Because of the high tannin content and anti-bacterial properties of the oak old country law advised its use to prolong life. Many items, including leather, were preserved with oak tannin. It is a very pleasant tonic but I doubt 'that all who drink this liqour each day will exceed one hundred years of life'.

It is useful as a mouth wash and gargle for the treatment of mouth ulcers, pharyngitis and tonsillitis.

Parsley Wine

3 gallons parsley heads
2 lbs. sultanas
10 lbs. sugar
2 tspns. grape tannin
3 tspns. malic acid
3 tspns. tartaric acid
2 tspns. yeast nutrient
1 tspn. Bentonite
Wine yeast

Proceed as for oak leaf wine.

Parsley Wine

Parsley is rich in minerals and vitamins. Is an aperient – stimulant – diuretic – antiseptic – carminative – emmenagogue – and expectorant.

The Egyptians used wild parsley in the treatment of complaints of the urinary tract.

Ancient physicians held this herb in great esteem perscribing it for dropsy, jaundice, rheumatism, to stimulate kidney function and to relieve the discomfort associated with menstruation. It is said that daily applications of a concoction of parsley in wine will cause freckles to disappear and clear the complexion. Tragus offered the following formula for a medicine in the treatment of jaundice, the falling sickness, dropsy, and stones of the kidneys. "Take of the seed of parsley, fennel, annise, and caraway, of each an ounce; of the roots of parsley, burnet saxifrage and caraway, of each an ounce and a half. Let the seeds be bruised and the roots washed and cut small, let them lay all night steeped in a bottle of wine and in the morning be boiled in a close earthenware vessel until a third part or more be wasted; which being strained and cleared take four ounces thereof morning and evening, first and last, abstaining from drink after it for three hours. This opens obstructions of the spleen, and expels the dropsy and jaundice by urine."

Parsnip Wine

15 lbs. parsnips
3 lbs. sultanas
10 lbs. sugar
2 tspns. grape tannin
3 tspns. citric acid
2 tspns. malic acid
2 tspns. tartaric acid
1 tspn. pectic enzyme
1 tspn. yeast nutrient
Wine yeast

Proceed as for blackberry wine. 8 ozs. of bruised ginger can be added to this recipe if desired.

Parsnip Wine

Made from cultivated parsnips although old country wine makers preferred the wild variety.

Be careful if deciding to make wild parsnip as it can easily be confused with other plants which are poisonous and of similar appearance to the novice. Hemlock has been mistaken for wild parsnip by some physicians in the past, as this plant contains some very obnoxious alkaloid compounds I doubt that their patients ever got better.

Parsnips are anodyne- carminative – cathartic – diuretic – galactagogue – and stomachic.

Pea Pod Wine

Very old traditional wine.

20 lbs. pea pods
4 lbs. sultanas
10 lbs. sugar approx.
3 tspns. citric acid
2 tspns. malic acid
2 tspns. tartaric acid
2 tspns. grape tannin
1 tspn. pectic enzyme
1 tspn. yeast nutrient
1 tspn. Bentonite
Wine yeast

Proceed as for oak leaf wine.

Pea Pod Wine

A very old, popular country wine and tonic, no wonder when considering some of the base ingredients. It is high in carbohydrates – vegetable protein – vitamin B1 (Thiamine), B2 (Riboflavin), Vitamin B6 (Pyridoxine), Niacin, (Nicotinic Acid), and contains the minerals Calcium (Ca.) Magnesium (Mg.), Phosphorous (P), Sodium (Na), (Trace), Sulphur (S) and Iron (Fe).

It is prescribed as a carminative, demulcent, depurative, nervine, appetiser and stomachic.

Recommended as a tonic for elderly persons, convalescents, especially those suffering from loss of appetite.

Peach Wine

30 lb. peaches
4 lb. raisins
9lb. sugar
2 tspns. citric acid
4 tspns. malic acid
2 tspns. tartaric acid
2 tspns. grape tannin
1 tspn. pectic enzyme
1 tspn. yeast nutrient
1 tspn. Bentonite

Proceed as for carrot wine.

Peach Wine

Peaches are expectorant – laxative – vermifuge – antispasmodic – sedative.

In ancient time the leaves and flowers including the fruit were used medicinally.

The leaves and flowers, boiled with sugar or honey to the consistency of a syrup, was said to have been a remedy often used by Louis XIV and Voltaire for the treatment of constipation.

Pear Wine

30 lbs. pears
4 lbs. raisins
9 lbs. sugar approx.
2 tspns. citric acid
4 tspns. malic acid
2 tspns. tartaric acid
2 tspns. grape tannin
1 tspn. pectic enzyme
1 tspn. yeast nutrient
1 tspn. Bentonite

Proceed as for carrot wine.

Pear Wine

Pears are aperient – demulcent – febrifuge – haemostatic – oxytocic – stomachic – vermifuge – vulnerary.

Culpepper claimed that adding pear wine to mushrooms when cooking made them less dangerous. Presumably this refered to the picking of toxic fungi mistakenly collected with the mushroom batch, the pear ingredients combating the toxins. I do not intend putting that particular remedy to the test. Apparently Galen used raw wild pears to heal fresh wounds but it is not clear whether he used the solid fruit or macerated it in wine before application as was his practice in many other remedies. The wine would almost certainly have assisted in the healing process as a disinfectant and anti-bacterial agent. Pear wine can be applied to the skin to combat rashes caused by allergies or plant reactions such as stinging nettles. The effect is soothing and relief is rapid.

Plum Wine

Quantity of ingredients as for damson wine. If making a desert wine rather than table wine, increase quantity of plums to twenty-five pounds.

Proceed as for blackberry wine.

Plum Wine

The plum is an appetiser – febrifuge – laxative – stomachic.

As in the well known use of the dried plum – prunes –, plums have been known for centuries to be a mild laxative and an aid to digestion.

An old recipe was to warm the wine, then add cinnamon, nutmeg, lemon peel and honey, the resulting delicious syrup will be extremely beneficial and without any unpleasant side effects.

Potato Wine

20 lbs. potatoes
4 lbs. sultanas
6 lbs. sugar
1 oz. Amylozyne
(starch reducing enzyme)
4 tspns. citric acid
3 tspns. malic acid
1 tspn. tartaric acid
2 tspns. grape tannin
1 tspn. pectic enzyme
1 tspn. yeast nutrient
Wine yeast

This recipe varies from all the usual rules of wine making and just goes to show that there are exceptions to every rule. The ingredients are boiled in this instance, and the addition of starch into the must is actually encouraged. This time however, the starch is broken down to sugar by a special enzyme, so that the yeast can ferment the starch 'out' of the must.

Method:

Scrub potatoes clean but do not peel. Boil until tender but not broken. This part can be carried out in batches if required. When off the boil place in preparation vessel, and add sugar, acids, nutrient and grape tannin. When temperature is down to 65° F., add enzymes and yeast. Allow to ferment in preparation vessel for three days, then transfer liquid to fermentation vessel and ferment down to required s.g. The must can be fed with sugar syrup in the latter stages of fermentation to obtain quite a high alcohol content if desired. Remember to use a yeast of high alcohol tolerance if latter stage is employed.

Potato Wine

Like the tomato when it was first introduced to this country, the potato was thought to be poisonous as it is in the same family of plants as belladona and henbane (Solanacea.) Apart from the natural caution of eating a tuberous night-shade the initial supplies were very expensive it is surprising therefore that the potato is universally eaten by most households everyday given it's early history. It is said that Oliver Cromwell valued the potato highly and even grew it in his garden.

Early physicians however were not slow in discovering the beneficial properties of this root and Gerard mentions the potato in his Herbal of 1596.

The early uses were for the treatment of diarrhoea, stomach ulcers and to combat chronic headaches or migraine.

Prune Wine

Although prunes are the dried fruit of plums, a wine of totally different colour and flavour is obtained.

Proceed as for plum wine.

Raisin Wine

15 lbs. raisins
2 tspns. citric acid
6 lbs. sugar approx.
1 tspn. pectic enzyme
1 tspn. yeast nutrient
Wine yeast
1 tspn. Bentonite

Method:

As the raisin is a dried grape it will probably form a balanced must on its own without further additions. However, it is advisable in wine making to leave nothing to chance, hence the additions of extra ingredients.

Rinse the raisins in warm water before placing them in the preparation vessel. Dissolve sugar, acid and nutrient and add to bulk. The s.g. should be carefully checked when adding sugar as the sugar contained by the dried fruit varies considerably. Add water to make up to mark, and add wine yeast when temperature reaches 65–70° F. After five days transfer to fermentation vessel.

When desired s.g. is reached add five Campden tablets and allow wine to clarify before placing in storage vessel.

Raspberry Wine

A radiant rosé wine, ideal to make when there is a glut of fruit in the garden and the freezer is overflowing.

15 lbs. raspberries
3 lbs. sultanas
10 lbs. sugar approx.
3 tspns. malic acid
2 tspns. tartaric acid
2 tspns. grape tannin
1 tspn. pectic enzyme
1 tspn. yeast nutrient
1 tspn. Bentonite
Wine yeast

Proceed as for blackberry wine using pulp fermentation.

Raspberry Wine

Raspberries are astringent – cardiac – febrifuge – laxative,

Raspberries are one of the few soft fruits truly native to the British Isles. Cultivation is thought to have started from the wild in the sixth century onwards, with selective cultivation taking place from around the 13th century. This was a medicine strictly for the ladies as early medicinal use was to relieve labour pains, improve lactation in nursing mothers and to reduce the risk of miscarriage.

Its astringent qualities later led to it being prescribed as a mouth wash, gargle and externally for the treatment of sores and rashes. It is also believed to be a cardiac tonic.

Red Currant Wine

Quantities as for blackcurrant, substituting redcurrants and sultanas for blackcurrants and raisins.

Makes a delightful rosé wine with a distinctive bouquet.

Proceed as for blackberry wine.

Red Currant Wine

Aperient – astringent – febrifuge – laxative – sialogogue – stomachic

Red currant wine diluted with equal parts of water (cooled from boiled), is a useful remedy for an upset stomach. The tonic can be sweetened with a little sugar or honey to taste if required.

In cases of gastric illness or extreme diarrhoea the above mixture is beneficial to combat dehydration and to cleanse the gastro-intestinal tract.

Providing the dosage is not exceeded it will not cause vomiting and should relieve the feelings of nausea. If vomiting should occur then dilute with an equal volume of water before administering again.

One tablespoonful to be taken every half hour whilst the patient is awake. If vomiting or diarrhoea absent then dosage can gradually be increased. If however the symptoms re-appear then reduce dosage back to the measure of one table-spoonful every half hour. For young or infirm people the more dilute version of the tonic should be administered. During the treatment and for the next twenty four hours no food should be given even if the appetite has returned. This will allow the intestine to regain equilibrium and cleanse the harmful bacteria. If food is ingested during that period the toxic bacteria may restart to multiply and the symptoms start all over again, much to the horror of the patient. The wine may also be used for a mouth wash, gargle and blood purifier.

Rhubarb Wine

I do not advocate the making of this wine as it can have a high level of extremely toxic acid (oxalic acid).

For those who insist on making this beverage then the sugar extraction method is recommended, as this will reduce the oxalic acid content of the must.*

Quantities and method as for peach wine.

*The wine is useful as a base for herbal lotions.

Rhubarb Wine

Rhubarb wine made from the stalks of the plant is a strong purgative and laxative. Old country wines and medicines employed the root which is less toxic than the stalks. Chinese physicians highly valued the root of rhubarb which was prescribed in one form or another for a multitude of disorders. Although European early herbalists believed it to be the same plant as that prescribed by the Chinese – it was in fact a different variety (Rheum Palmatum).

Fortunately for the early apothecaries who copied the ancient Oriental prescriptions, the European variety has very much the same properties.

Rice Wine

5 lbs. rice
3 lbs. sultanas
10 lbs. sugar approx.
3 tspns. citric acid
2 tspns. malic acid
1 tspn. tartaric acid
1 tspn. grape tannin
Enzyme for pectin and starch
1 tspn. yeast nutrient
Wine yeast

Method:

Rinse sultanas in warm water that has been cooled from boiled, and add to preparation vessel with rice. Dissolve sugar, acids, tannin and wine nutrient and add to bulk. Add enzymes and make up to the mark with water. Switch on heat and when temperature reaches 65–70° F., add wine yeast. Stir well each day for seven days, then transfer to fermentation vessel under airlock, taking care not to disturb lees. Ferment to an s.g. of 1.00, then add five Campden tablets and Bentonite if required, although this wine clears well without assistance. Transfer to storage vessel and adjust if required as described in previous recipes.

This wine improves with keeping, and is superb at its peak after three years.

Rice Wine

Rice sustains a large proportion of the human race in providing most of their dietary needs i.e. carbohydrates, proteins, essential amino acids, vitamins and minerals. Rice wine is a useful tonic, especially for those suffering from exhaustion, a blood cleanser and useful in relaxing patients suffering from Hypertension.

For young or elderly people suffering loss of appetite or weakness due to prolonged sickness, a tonic comprising one part rice wine to two parts water administered at regular intervals should work wonders.

Dosage depends on the size and age of the patient but an eggcupful would be a reasonable dosage at hourly intervals to start with. Do not increase the frequency of dosage or increase the quantity even if patient complains of thirst. If persistent, for further or increased quantities, administer water. The patient is already on the way to recovery if complaining in this way.

Rosehip Wine

15 lbs. rosehips
4 lbs. sultanas
10 lbs. sugar
3 tspns. citric acid
3 tspns. malic acid
1 tspn. tartaric acid
1 tspn. grape tannin
1 tspn. wine nutrient
1 tspn. Bentonite
Wine yeast

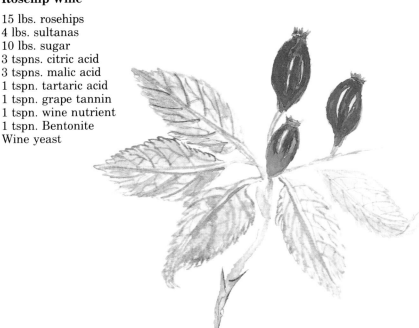

Method:

Proceed as for rice wine.

A smooth wine high in minerals and vitamins with subsequent good curative properties.

Rosehip Wine

As everyone knows rosehips are high in vitamin C, and is therefore useful in combating the worst effects of a feverish cold. Add honey or sugar to rosehip wine to the consistency of a syrup and take one tablespoonful as required. This remedy is also useful for treating a dry or sore throat.

It is prescribed as a carminative and diuretic.

The diuretic property is particularly useful as it can combat uric acid accumulation without irritation to the kidneys. Made into a poultice with rice flour and crushed mustard seed it is a great reliever of rheumatic pains and aching joints. Crush mustard seeds to a fine powder, weigh then add ten times that weight of rice powder. Add rosehip wine stirring all the time until a thick paste is obtained. Spread paste on clean linen or gauze (preferably sterilized) and apply to affected area to be treated. Repeat treatment as often as required.

If symptoms persist after several treatments then seek professional advice.

The seeds or achenes of the hips when dried and reduced to a powder were added to wine and allowed to infuse for twenty four hours. This remedy was a very old prescription for gravel, kidney stones and renal colic.

The above concoction mixed with honey and taken as a syrup is a very effective vermifuge without any unpleasant side effects or irritation to the small intestine.

Rose Petal Wine

An appetizing wine with a lovely fragrance. Quantity of ingredients as for marigold wine.

Proceed as for clover wine.

Rose Petal Wine

An ancient medicine prescribed in many countries. Arab physicians prescribed it for tuberculosis and other pulmonary complaints. Modern science has shown that rose petals have natural anti-biotic properties. In Europe it was widely prescribed to combat dizziness and as a heart and nerve tonic. The early Romans used a decoction of rose petals in wine to relieve toothache and as a mouthwash and gargle. Applied to the temples this decoction was thought to relieve headaches.

Sloe Wine

12 lbs. sloes
10 lbs. sugar approx.
3 tspns. citric acid
3 tspns. malic acid
1 tspn. tartaric acid
1 tspn. grape tannin
1 tspn. pectic enzyme
1 tspn. yeast nutrient
1 tspn. Bentonite
Wine yeast

Method: Proceed as for blackberry wine using pulp fermentation method.

Sloe Wine

Sloe wine is an excellent remedy for a sore throat as is sloe gin. I use sloe wine to make up the bulk of sloe gin because of the high price of gin these days.

Medicinal uses; aperient – astringent – diaphoretic – diuretic – stomachic.

Strawberry Wine

A light wine with superb bouquet, suitable for producing a good sparkling wine. Quantities as for raspberry wine. Proceed as for blackberry wine.

Strawberry Wine

Astringent – diuretic – tonic – analgesic – demulcent.

Called a 'blessing of the gods' by the famous botanist Linne (1707–1778) after he was cured of the gout by a diet of strawberries. Prescribed for treatment of the liver, kidneys, rheumatism, gout, and angina.

Culpepper said of the strawberry. "The leaves and roots boiled in wine and water and drank, do cool the liver and the blood. (Strawberries are now known to contain iron and salicylic acid) and assuage all inflammations in the reins and bladder, provoke urine, and allay the heat and sharpness thereof. The same also being drank stays the bloody flux and womens courses and helps the swelling of the spleen."

Tea Wine

1 gallon of strong tea
4 lbs. sultanas
10 lbs. sugar approx.
3 tspns. citric acid
2 tspns. malic acid
1 tspn. pectic enzyme
Wine yeast

Proceed as for raisin wine.

Tea Wine

The black tea common to this country is in fact the fermented leaves of the plant Thea Sinensia, but leaves which are green in their natural state will also produce a good wine. The difficulty in this country is obtaining the plant fresh. Tea is astringent – tonic – stimulant – nervine.

The caffeine content of tea makes it a strong stimulant. Drunk in large quantities it has known to cause strong addiction. To those who have been deprived of tea for only a short period withdrawal symptoms such as depression and irritability have been observed. Our grandmothers would always put the kettle on for a strong cup of tea whenever a crisis loomed, though presumably they had no knowledge of the caffeine content. The same practice is carried out today in many homes, and is a good example of how recipes were known to be instinctively right and were passed down from one generation to another, without any specific scientific knowledge or questioning. Because of the tannin content of tea wine it is useful for mixing with other wines lacking in this ingredient.

Wheat Wine

2 lbs. wheat
4 lbs. sultanas
8 lbs. sugar approx.
3 tspns. citric acid
3 tspns. malic acid
2 tspns. grape tannin
1 tspn. pectic enzyme
1 tspn. yeast nutrient
1 tspn. Bentonite
Wine yeast

Method:

Dissolve sugar, acids, tannin and nutrient in water and add to wheat, and rinsed sultanas, in preparation vessel.

Switch on heat and when temperature reaches 65° F., add wine yeast. Allow to ferment for ten days, rousing the wine each day. Transfer to fermentation vessel under airlock and ferment to a s.g. of 1.00. Add four Campden tablets and Bentonite and when clear transfer to storage vessel.

Ready to drink after a few months, but does not reach maturity for at least a year.

Wheat Wine

Galen used the pressed oil from wheat to treat ring worm and skin ulcers. Ancient physicians boiled wheat flour in water to make poultices for skin eruptions. It was also boiled in wine vinegar for the treatment of skin conditions, removal of spots and freckles.

Culpepper also recommended wheat for the treatment of the skin though I doubt that he ever cured leprosy with the following recipe. If a cure was affected it was probably wrongly diagnosed. 'The bran of wheat meal steeped in sharp vinegar and then bound in a linen cloth and rubbed on those places that have the scurf, morphew, scabs or leprosy, will take them away the body being first well purged and prepared'.

71

Wine Making Using Natural Substances

For the purists who wish to make their wine only from natural substances without the addition of chemicals (and can afford the luxury), the recipes can be altered with the following alternatives.

When substituting the alternative ingredients in any of the recipes, the methods remain unchanged.

In place of sugar, substitute honey or a mixture of honey and grape juice.

12 ozs. honey = 1 lbs. sugar

or

7½ lbs. honey = 10 lbs. sugar.

Alternatively

5 lbs. honey + 5 pints grape juice = 10 lbs. sugar.

Substitute strong tea for grape tannin.

2 cups strong tea = 1 tspn. grape tannin.

Substitute lemon juice for citric acid.

Substitute apple juice for malic acid.

In place of yeast nutrient use yeast extract, or a teaspoonful of Marmite. Another alternative is to use malt extract.

The recipes on the preceding pages are for single fruit but mixtures work well, try:

Blackberry and elderberry

Elderberry and sloe

Elderberry and blackcurrant

(or a mixture of all four).

Addition of banana will impart body to country wines.

All quantities are expressed in Imperial measures. For those who are more familiar with metric the following conversion table will alow for easy conversion of recipes.

Weights		Liquid Measure	
Metric	*Imperial*	*Metric*	*Imperial*
12 g.	½ oz.	25 ml.	1 fl. oz.
25 g.	1 oz.	50 ml.	2 fl. oz.
112 g.	4 ozs.	75 ml.	3 fl. oz.
225 g.	8 ozs.	100 ml.	4 fl. oz.
450 g.	1 lb.	140 ml.	5 fl. oz.
1 kg.	2 lbs. 3 ozs.	275 ml.	½ pt.
3.6 kg.	8 lbs.	575 ml.	1 pt.
4.5 kg.	10 lbs.	1 ltr.	1¾ pt.
		4.5 ltr.	1 gallon

Faults and Remedies

If you have followed the instructions carefully, you should not need to refer to this section. However, faults or errors do occur and this section will help you to overcome the common ones.

If fermentation ceases before required hydrometer reading is reached proceed through the following checks.

(a) Check that nutrient was added and check acidity level. If acid level indicated is low or neutral add one level teaspoonful of citric acid and the same amount of malic acid plus half a teaspoonful of grape tannin. It is best to dissolve these ingredients in a small quantity of the must and then return to the bulk.

(b) Check temperature and ensure heater and thermostat are working correctly. If heater was not working then fermentation should start within twenty four hours once heat is supplied.

(c) Aerate the wine (rouse the wine), by pouring into another sterilized container, alternatively stir bulk with a beating action on the surface to introduce air and thereby oxygenate. Leave for twenty-four hours after which time a slow fermentation should start, gaining in vigour as the yeast multiplies.

(d) Check hydrometer reading and if sugar content is on or above the recommended level then dilute with water to reduce level.

(e) If none of the above has the desired result, it is likely that the yeast itself is at fault. Prepare fresh yeast and add this to the bulk.

Other faults such as oiliness, flower like chains of powder on the surface* or wine smelling or tasting of vinegar means that the wine has been infected by bacteria. Unlike many books on the subject of home wine making it is not intended to give patent 'cure alls' for bad wine as the object is to achieve a quality product.

The wine exhibiting any of the faults mentioned above is bad and infected. Throw it away. Sterilize all utensils immediately and start a new batch.

Some minor problems not associated with bacterial infection can be overcome, such as the finished wine tasting flat and lacking bite.

Take small wine glasses of the bulk, and to one add a small amount of tannin, to another add a small amount of citric acid, and to another a few drops of lactic acid. To another row of glasses pour some of the treated wine to obtain mixtures. Taste each in turn clearing the palate between each tasting. Eventually a blending will be discovered that is pleasing, but only by developing an educated palate by this trial and error method plus experience can it immediately be determined what is required to correct balance and in what quantities.

If the wine lacks body, it can be blended with a full-bodied wine. Once again experiment with various mixtures until a satisfactory blend is achieved. It is well worth noting that once two wines have been mixed it can take up to six months to blend completely.

Bacteria may be introduced by the vinegar fly Drosophila Melanogaster. A small fly always present in compost heaps or decaying fruit.

They often appear miraculously when producing a must even when all doors or windows are shut. I believe they are probably lying dormant and hidden amongst the fruit, and are awakened by the processing.

*Do not confuse this with the Sherry "flor" caused by the addition of air to a maturing wine, a white to greenish fungus apparent on the surface of the wine. This is a desirable effect if you are producing a sherry-type wine.

Essential Vitamins and Minerals of Wine Ingredients

Apart from the additional ingredients obtained by infusion of herbs, the basic ingredients of the wine itself can supply anything up to seven vitamins and eight minerals. It therefore follows that a wine prepared from two sets of ingredients may contain twice as many as this. For example in carrot and potato wine, carrots contain vitamin A, vitamin B2, vitamin B6, vitamin C, niacin, and the minerals, calcium, magnesium, phosphorous, potassium, sodium, copper, iron and manganese.

Potatoes contain vitamin B1, vitamin B2, vitamin B6, vitamin B12, plus several other minerals including zinc.

The term mineral is used in the nutritional sense to mean any chemical necessary for the proper functioning of the body.

At this stage it is best to explain that many of the minerals mentioned in the wine ingredients are in minuscule amounts, nevertheless in many instances the body requires only minute doses to maintain healthy growth, and indeed any excesses could be extremely toxic.

Returning to the carrot and potato wine, apart from the minerals and vitamins contained in those ingredients, yeast itself is a source of many vitamins including B1, B2, B6, B12, vitamin D and niacin.

In order to explain the medicinal uses of the various wines, some understanding of essential vitamins and minerals and the part they play in maintaining a healthy system is necessary.

Read on in order to discover which wine ingredients contain the aforementioned vitamins and minerals.

Vitamin A – **Axerophthol**

The essential ingredient obtained is carotene which is then converted into vitamin A in the body. It plays an essential role in the formation of visual purple in the retina of the eye, and is therefore used in the treatment of night blindness and other eye disorders. It is also reputed to have been prescribed to military personnel in the war to improve their night vision on operations after dark. May be considered to act achiefly as a regulator of the growth of epitherial tissues, thereby keeping the outer layers of tissues and organs healthy. Promotes growth in bones, skin, hair, and teeth.

Is an aid in the treatment of emphysemia and hyperthrodoxin.

As an external agent is excellent for the treatment of acne, boils, impetigo, carbuncles, ulcers, and the removal of age spots.

Instead of expensive cosmetic lotions to combat ageing of the skin, try a mixture of unfiltered (hazed; carrot and apple wine with the herbs infused of angelica, mint and lady's mantle.

Massage lotion on to facial skin and allow to dry, then rinse in cold water. Treatment should be carried out for at least three weeks for full benefit to be noticed, although some improvement can be felt by the recipient after only one or two treatments.

Although a certain amount of glycerine is present in the fermented liquid, the alcohol can have a drying and over degreasing effect on patients with a very dry skin, a spoonful of glycerine to a cupful of lotion should be added to counteract this effect.

74

This lotion cleared my badly chapped hands after only two applications, whereas proprietary creams borrowed from my wife before this trial had only kept the symptoms in check without effecting a cure. Unfortunately I have not had the resource of time or sufficient patience to experiment further with these skin lotions, especially as I need to monitor their effects, but I hope that many readers will try these remedies and I may receive further feedback of information and develop improvements. As the results of tests to date are physically apparent I have discounted any placebo influences.

Toxicity factor discussed earlier is confirmed by the effects of excess vitamin A, the symptoms of which are hair loss, scaly skin, blurred vision, rashes, and bone pain.

Wine ingredients containing Vitamin A are: carrots, apricots, nettle, elder-berries, dandelion, cranberry, blueberry, cowslip and red currant.

Herbs containing vitmain A are: spearmint, parsley, chicory and broccoli.

Vitamin B₁ **Thiamine**

Essential for the proper functioning of neurological processes and has been used in the treatment of nervous diseases. Patients suffering from delirium tremens have responded well with vitamin B1 treatment. Is useful to combat air or sea sickness and has been used in the treatment of neuralgia, hyperthyroidism, allergies, and herpes.

Toxicity factor. As it is soluble in water any excesses are excreted and not stored to any large degree in the body. In the rarely recorded excess, however, the symptoms here again line up with the treatment factor, namely tremors, herpes, oedema, nervousness, rapid heart beat, and allergies.

Wine ingredients containing vitamin B1 are: barley, potato, pea, fig, raisins, dandelion, pineapple, orange, parsnip and yeast.

Vitamin B2. **Riboflavin**

Necessary for the promotion of healthy skin, nails and hair, and assisting growth of bones and reproductive processes. Is beneficial to vision and is said to alleviate eye fatigue. Also useful to a lesser extent in the treatment of acne, and muscle cramps.

No known toxicity factors.

Wine ingredients containing vitamin B2 are: apricots, peas, date, fig, raspberry, parsnip, potato, raisin and yeast.

Vitamin B3. Niacin (nicotinic acid)

One kilogram of yeast contains 825 mg. of nicotinic acid. Nicotinic acid is synthesized in the intestine and the amino acid tryptophane is a precursor of nicotinic acid.

Is used in the treatment of migraine headaches, reduction of high blood pressure, tinnitus, meneres syndrome (vertigo). Reduction of cholesterol and stomatitis associated with chronic alcoholism. It is also said to be essential for the synthesis of sex hormones.

Is non toxic even in large doses.

Wine ingredients containing vitamin B3 are: wheat, rice, apricots, pea, date, potato, carrot, peaches, raisins and yeast

Vitamin B5. Panothenic Acid

This vitamin has been shown to have an 'anti grey hair' factor in various species. Useful for the treatment of a variety of complaints which include respiratory, bronchial, and liver disorders. Has been used both externally and internally in the treatment of achrohotrichia, and alopecia as well as other disorders of the hair.

No known toxicity factor.

Main source in wine ingredients are: wheat yeast, pea, barley, rice, potato and carrot.

Vitamin B6. Pyridoxine

Useful in the treatment of nervous and muscular disorders associated with muscular dystrophy, Parkinson's disease, and nausea. It also promotes synthesis of anti-ageing nucleic acids, and is used in the treatment of radiation sickness.

Wine ingredients as for B5.

No known toxicity.

Vitamin B12. Cyanocobalamin

Used widely in the treatment of anaemia as it helps in the regeneration of red blood cells. Has also been prescribed as an appetite enhancer, relief of irritability, and is claimed to improve concentration and memory.

No known toxicity.

Wine ingredients contain only small amounts of this vitamin.

Herb additive to increase concentration common comfrey.

Vitamin B17. Laetrile

Chemically a compound of two sugar molecules: one aldehyde, the other cyanide called an amygdolin. The cyanide element gives the almond smell and flavour to the pips and to a lesser amount the fruit of cherries, apricots, apples and plums.

For this reason a few cracked kernels or pips are often added with the fruit in wine recipes as flavouring. Excess of this chemical should be avoided however as cyanide is a very potent poison.

Laetrile is used in the treatment of certain cancers.

Is an effective medicine in the treatment of stomach upsets and menstrual pains.

Vitamin C. Ascorbic Acid

The value of this vitamin and its uses are almost too many to enumerate. The main treatment values are for:

Treatment of wounds and burns
Gastro–intestinal disorders
Reduction of blood cholesterol
Dental and oral conditions
Rheumatism
Ophthalmology–corneal conditions
Prevention of viral and bacterial infections
Lowering incidence of blood clots
Anti-ageing agent by enabling protein cells to bond together
Prevention of scurvy
Reduces effects of allergies

Asthmatic attacks

Antidote to metal and benzene poisoning by absorption

Cancer depressant.

Toxicity factor

Excessive dose can cause skin rashes, diarrhoea, kidney stones, and excess urination.

Main source of this vitamin in wine ingredients are: blueberry, blackberry, blackcurrant, elderberry, dandelion, carrot, raspberry, rose hip, nettle, lemon, orange and strawberry.

Vitamin D. Califerol

The principal use of vitamin D is in the prophylosis and treatment of calcium, phosphorous metabolism, in other words, the proper utilisation of these elements for strong bones and teeth. Used in the treatment and prevention especially in younger children of rickets, spasmophylia, and tetany. The need for this vitamin is considerably increased during pregnancy.

Aids in the assimilation of vitamin A and is said to assist with the prevention of the common cold. Senile osteoporosis is due to the lack of this vitamin; it is therefore essential for elderly people to have sufficient in their diet.

Toxicity factor. Vomiting, diarrhoea, sore eyes, abnormal calcium deposits in organs.

Main source of this vitamin in wine ingredients: Although this vitamin does not occur to any extent in usual wine ingredients, yeast is a major source of ergosterol which is converted to vitamin D by the action of ultra violet light.

Vitamin E. Tocopherol

Acts primarily through an enzyme system as a physiological anti-oxidant and is therefore an anti-ageing agent. Used to prevent habitual abortion, prevents and dissolves blood clots, accelerates the healing of burns, alleviates fatigue, treatment of fibrositis, in men improves the mobility, morphology, and count of sperm in infertile cases.

Is useful in the treatment of the menopause syndrome.

No known toxicity factor.

Main source in wine ingredients: apples, barley, nettle.

The increase in male sperm attributed to this vitamin explains why it is considered by some to be an aphrodisiac.

Whilst on the subject of aphrodisiacs it is worth while mentioning three other vitamins which are really classed in the vitamin B complex, they are folic acid, inisitol PABA (para-aminobenzic acid). These vitamins are present in yeast and promote healthy skin and hair, they also assist in the fertility of men and the formation of male sex hormones.

Vitamin H. Biotin

Used to combat dermatitis. Promotes healthy hair. Recent research has shown that this vitamin can combat hair fall out.

Yeast contains vitamin H.

Vitamin K. Konakion

Is necessary for the formation by the liver of prothrombin, which in turn is essential to the functioning of the blood clotting mechanism. Is used in the treatment of internal haemorrhages and in reducing excessive menstrual flow, and the treatment of chilblains.

Many herbs contain konakion.

Wine source: nettle leaves (young).

Vitamin P

One of the C complex. Flavonoids produce the yellow and orange colour in citrus fruits. Used in the treatment of bleeding gums, helps to resist infection and in the treatment of oedema and dizziness due to disease of the inner ear.

No known toxicity.

Wine source: citrus fruit.

Tryptophan

An essential amino-acid used by the brain along with vitamin B6 (niacin), and magnesium to produce serotin, a neuro-transmitter that carries messages between the brain and the bio-chemical mechanisms of sleep. Can therefore help to induce natural sleep, aids in reducing anxiety symptoms and acts as an anti-depressant.

Wine source: banana.

Lysine

Is a vital amino acid in the make-up of body proteins. Aids the production of anti-bodies, hormones and enzymes.

Is associated with growth and tissue repair.

Has been used for alleviating infertility and promoting better concentration.

Wine source: banana.

Arginine

Similar uses and properties as lysine, especially essential for men, since seminal fluids contain as much as 80% of this proteic acid.

Aids in the treatment of infertility in males, aids in immune response and wound healing.

Natural growth hormone levels decrease with age until around the fiftieth year production virtually stops.

Supplementing the aminoacids and vitamins that stimulate the release of these hormones can stimulate the production to the levels of a young adult. It is said that the peak secretion of growth hormones is reached approximately two hours after the onset of natural sleep.

The main growth hormone release agents are ornithine, arginine, tryptophan, glycine, and tyrosine synergistically with vitmain B6, vitamin C, and the elements calcium, magnesium, potassium and zinc.

To obtain a wine containing all the required ingredients will necessitate blending a variety of wines with the desired constituents. As it is beyond the scope of domestic producers to determine the exact concentrations of the beneficial ingredients once a certain wine is produced, it is best to start with a blend of equal parts initially, record the results then alter the formulation by one extra measure of each of the ingredients in turn taking measurements of effects and recording at each stage until the desired balance is reached.

Nettle

Minerals

In terms of nutrition, minerals refer to the chemical elements necessary for the proper growth and functioning of the body.

As with other beneficial elements for good health, excessive quantities are not desirable, indeed many elements such as molybdenum make up less than five parts per thousand of body weight. Trace elements, many of which the exact function is still undetermined but it is known are necessary for good health, can be as small as one part per hundred thousandth of body weight.

Calcium (Ca.)

As every school child will know, it is vital for the formation of good bones and teeth. The other known functions include control of fluids through cell walls, functioning of muscles, nerve tissues and clotting of blood.

Wine ingredients containing calcium: fig, elderberry, coltsfoot, nettle, citrus fruit, pea and rose hip.

Chlorine (Cl.)

Chlorine is ingested with sodium when consuming common salt (also iodine if using table salt).

Chlorine in its chemically uncombined state is a gas which forms chlorides; it is these compounds which maintain the balance of fluids inside and outside of cell walls by osmosis.

Hydrogen chloride or hydrocholic acid is contained in gastric juices.

Wine ingredients containing chlorine: banana and carrot.

In general adequate amounts of sodium and chlorine are ingested as common salt added to foodstuffs. Indeed many maintain that too much salt is consumed.

Iodine (I.)

Iodine deficiency causes goiter. It is important for the proper functioning of reproduction and lactation.

The quantities of iodine in plants is governed by the concentration in the soil in which they are grown.

Iron (Fe.)

Is essential for the formation of haemoglobin in the blood, and is also necessary in the production of enzymes for energy and proper muscle functioning.

Wine ingredients containing iron: apricot, blackberry, date, elderberry, fig, pea, plum, raisin and blackcurrant.

Magnesium (Mg.)

Acts as an enzyme activator for the maintenance and formation of protein.

Wine ingredients containing magnesium: barley, pea, fig, date, apricot, apple, banana, blackberry, cherry, raspberry, peach, potato, parsnip and citrus fruit.

Manganese (Mn.)

Vital for healthy bone formation.
Wine ingredients containing manganese: nettle leaves.

Phosphorous (P.)

Necessary for the proper neurological functions of the brain, enzyme formation, muscular development, and as a constituent of bones and teeth.
Wine ingredients containing phosphorous: pea, apricot, fig, raisin, date, elderberry, potato, apple, banana, blackberry and citrus fruits.

Potassium (K.)

Essential for the pH balance of fluids in cells and promotes enzyme reactions in the body.
Wine ingredietns containing potassium: apricot, fig, date, raisin, banana, potato, carrot, elderberry, cherry, blueberry and blackberry.

Sodium (Na.)

Vital for correct nerve and muscle functioning. Sodium acts as a regulator in the retention of body fluids, and with potassium maintains equilibrium of fluids inside and outside of cells.
Common salt (see chlorine), provides more than sufficient sodium for our needs and is not required as a wine ingredient.

Sulphur (S.)

Is involved in the correct formation of bone structure, blood clotting and muscle metabolism.
Wine ingredients containing sulphur, pea, wheat, barley, fig, date and nettle (young).

Zinc (Zn.)

Necessary for the proper functioning of the reproductive system and the manufacture of body proteins.
Wine ingredient for zinc: nettle (young leaves).

Medicinal Herbs

The listing of medicinal herbs is in no way intended to be comprehensive as there are many books already published on medicinal uses. A few of the most useful or little known herbs are listed here as they are often omitted in other works.

AGRIMONY. Agrimonia eupatoria (liver wort)
Height: Two feet.
Medicinal part: Foliage.

Used for complaints of the liver, hence its name liver wort (Wort – Anglo-Saxon name for plant). Modern scientific analysis has shown that ancient physicians were correct in the use of the plant as it contains a diurectic drug.

ANGELICA. Angelica archangelica.
Height: Four feet.
Medicinal part: Fresh leaves and stems for angina and heart burn.
Roots for digestion and blood cleansing.

BALM or LEMON BALM. Melissa Officianalis,
Height: 1½ ft.
Medicinal part: Leaves.

Main uses of this herb is in the treatment of the nervous system. Roots for digestion and blood cleansing.
For insomnia and nervous indigestion soak two ounces of leaves in a cupful of wine for eight to twelve hours. Decant from the solids and bottle. Take one tablespoonful before retiring each night. Chamomile can also be added to the liquor if required. In order to obtain a pleasant tasting remedy, choose a wine for the base which will not be adversely affected by the lemon flavour. It is also important to remember that the medicinal properties of the base wine do not conflict with the properties of the herbs employed. In this case for example a euphoriant or one recommended for energy should be avoided as the particular requirements are for a calming effect.

BARTSIA Odontis verna
Height: two feet.
Medicinal part: Leaves and flowers.

Used for pain relief and specifically to combat toothache, hence the botanical name given to the plant by the early Romans Odontis (of the teeth).

BASIL. Acinos arvensis.
Height: one foot
Medicinal part: Whole plant.

Steeped in wine, used for combating persistent feeling of nausea. One liqueur glassful taken every four hours until symptoms cease.

BAY. Laurus nobilis.
Height: Slow growing usually trimmed as a bush or standard.
Medicinal part: Leaves and berries.

Like balm can be used to cure insomnia. Culpepper claimed that the berries were effective in the treatment of wasp stings and the diarist, John Evelyn, recommended its use against the aggue (feuze).

BELL HEATHER. Erica cinerea.
Height: one foot.
Medicinal part: Flowers and stems.

The foliage has been used for centuries in the treatment of rheumatic fever, kidney and bladder inflammations.

BETONY. Stachys officinalis. (Bishopwort).
Height: three feet.
Medicinal part: Leaves.

Cultivated by monks, because of the many medicinal values, it may still be found to this day growing around Abbeys. Hence its name BISHOPWORT (Wort – Anglo-saxon – plant).
   Will quickly reduce a fever, and is beneficial in the treatment of digestive and liver complaints.

BIRTHWORT. Aristolochia Clematitis.
Height: Three feet.
Medicinal part: Rootstock,

The botanical name comes from the Greek 'Best Birth', which gives a clue to the ancient use of this herb – used to promote uterine contractions.
   The ancient Egyptians used it in the treatment of difficult childbirth and for the treatment of snake bite and wounds. The use of this plant is not recommended without proper medical supervision as it contains very potent drugs.

BUGLE. Ajuga reptans.
Height: Six inches.
Medicinal part: Leaves.

Bugle was the main ingredient of the 17th century TRAUMATIC DECOCTION wound healing drink.
Is said to be useful for the treatment of ulcers, bruises, and promoting milk in nursing mothers.

BUGLOSS. Vipers bugloss. Echium Vulgare.

A member of the borage family, the scientific name Echium is from the Greek, Echio (A viper). It was considered to be an antidote to the bite of the viper. It is a remedy which I do not wish to verify. BUGLOS (Anchusa Arvensis), is also of Greek origin, signifying an ox tongue from the shape and texture of the leaves.

According to Dioscorides, the early writer on medicine, it was a preventative to snake bite as well as antidote. To the 17th century herbalist William Coles, the stem of Vipers Bugloss is 'speckled like a serpent's skin which, according to The Doctrine of Signatures was proof of its value against snake venom. So too was the angular nutlet, produced as seed, which was thought to resemble the head of a snake thus reinforcing the plants use. Early herbalists claimed that an infusion of seeds in wine was able to drive away sadness and melancholy. I dare say that the effectiveness of this remedy depended on the quantity of wine consumed!

BURDOCK. Arctium lappa – A. minus
Height: (Depending on type), up to four feet.
Medicinal part: Stalks and roots.
An essence made from the plant is used in the drink burdock and dandelion, an old tonic, which is still popular to this day in the north of the country.

The roots are believed to be useful for preparing an aphrodisiac. A tonic, useful for the expulsion of accumulated toxins in the body, can be made by grating the fresh root and soaking in wine. Quantities suggested are 20 grams of root per litre of wine. Allowed to soak for forty eight to seventy two hours, the liquor is separated from the solids and the pulp squeezed to extract all the liquid using a sterilized muslin cloth. The dose indicated is one 5 ml. teaspoonful four times a day. Do not be disturbed if after two days of treatment a peculiar taste develops in the mouth and bad breath is apparent, this is only one of the harmless side effects concerned with the de-toxification of the body.

CARAWAY. Carum carvis.
Height: one to two feet.
Medicinal part: Seeds.

The seed is often employed as a flavouring in cakes. An infusion of seeds in wine is effective against painful indigestion. Culpepper prescribed if for flatulence.

CARROT. (WILD). Daucus Carotin. For garden carrot see wine section.
Height: two to three feet.
Medicinal part: The whole plant.

The juice taken from the plant and mixed with an equal quantity of wine makes a good antiseptic, gargle, and mouth wash.

CHAMOMILE. Chamaelum Nobile.
Height: Ground trailing.
Medicinal part: Foliage.

Chamomile is a mild sedative and tranquillizer effective against headaches.

Infuse a handful of the plant in one litre of blueberry wine for forty eight hours then decant liquid into a dark glass bottle, keep away from daylight and store in the cool.

Drink one wineglassful at slightly above room temperature to relieve tiredness, stress and exhaustion.

CHIVES. Allium schoenoprasum.
Height: One foot.
Medicinal part: Leaves.

Contains iron and arsenic (in harmless quantities), the latter ingredient probably explains its early use for the treatment of fevers and dysentery.

Is a good aid to appetite and digestion. If used in wine it is best mixed with other herbs containing the required medicinal properties to mask the onion flavour.

COMFREY. Symphytum Officinalis.
Height: Two to three feet.
Medicinal part: Rootstock.

Prepare a decoction of the root for digestive and stomach problems. It has also been used in the treatment of hematuria leucorrhea, ulcers and dysentry.
Dosage: Twenty grammes of fresh root or ten grammes of dried root to one half a litre of wine. Choose wine with complimentary properties to the form of treatment required.

One wineglassful taken three times a day will get rid of a persistent cough. For digestive problems take one wineglassful before meals. To reduce excessive menstrual flow take one liqueur glassful morning and night.

Further uses for this herb are described by its old country names, bruisewort and knit-bone. The ability of this plant to aid in the repair of fractured bones and to stop haemorrhaging is now being taken seriously after the discovery that it contained allantoin, which is known to help tissue formation and accelerate the healing of wounds. The botanical name, given many years before chemical analysis was available, Symphitum means 'I cause to grow together'.

CORIANDER. Coriandrum Sativum.
Height: 1–1½ ft.
Medicinal part: Seed.

Only use the fully ripened seed as it has a disagreeable smell when green.

The ancient Egyptians believed it to be an aphrodisiac and carminative. The use of this seed dates back thousands of years being added to wine for flavouring, and or medicinal reasons, mentioned in the bible.

Archeologists discovered the seeds in remains of food dating back to Neolithic times.

It is a very useful aid to digestion as it stimulates the flow of bile. The crushed seed, added to wine, makes an excellent marianade for meat especially useful if the meat lacks flavour or requires tenderising.

COWSLIP. Primula veris.
(See wine section for medicinal properties.)

CREEPING THISTLE. Cirsium arvense.
Height: up to four feet.
Medicinal part: Roots.

An extract of the essential ingredients in wine is an ancient nerve tonic. One ounce of root to half a litre of wine. Grate the root after washing in clean cold water cooled from boiling. Cover with wine and leave for twelve hours. Decant the liquid and squeeze the pulp to extract remaining wine. One tablespoonful every four hours will work wonders.

DANDELION. Taraxacum officinalis.

It has probably been noticed by now that many of the botanical names end with the word officinalis. This is a legacy from the days of the apothecaries, meaning it is sold in the shop, as an official tried medical remedy.

Medical properties of Dandelion: see wine section.

DAISY. Bellis perenis.

Perhaps because it is so common and considered a nuisance on lawns that the beauty of the daisy is overlooked.
The Latin name is more fitting for this noble flower Bellis derived from 'beautiful'.
    Culpepper believed that the daisy was a gift to mankind being such a useful herb, with many medicinal properties.
    He wrote of the daisy, 'Boiled in asses milk it is very effectual in the consumption of the lungs. "good luck with the milking!"'.

ELM. Ulmus Procea. Ulmus glabra-Wych Elm.
Medicinal part: Bark and leaves.

Usually grown as a tree but it can be pruned and trained as a shrub. I grow mine as part of a hedge.
    Soak bark (1 oz. to one litre), in wine for three days for the treatment of skin problems and cold sores.
    The leaves soaked in wine to the same proportions as above for twenty four hours, can be taken internally for the same conditions. Use a dry white wine of high alcohol content (12% to 14%).
Dosage: One liqueur glassful twice a day.

EVENING PRIMROSE. Oenothera biennis.
Height; From one to five feet.
Medicinal part: Plant and flowers.

See information under anti-ageing lotion.
Useful on its own or in combination with other herbs, various lotions and creams have been made for the cosmetic and medical treatment of the skin.
    An infusion of the plant in wine has been used to cure depression.

FENNEL. Foeniculum vulgare.
Height: Four feet.
Medicinal part: Seeds.

Used to relieve abdominal pains and as a gargle for sore throats. An infusion of the seeds in barley wine can be used to relieve rheumatic pains and aching joints.

FOXGLOVE. Digitalis purpurea.
Height: Up to five feet.

On no account should any attempt be made to use this plant unless medically qualified to do so.

GERMANDER SPEEDWELL. Veronica chamaedrys.
SPEEDWELL. Veronica Officinalis.
Height: One foot.
Medicinal part: Plant and flowers.

The term speedwell refers to the plants medicinal properties and value for quickly healing wounds and treating respiratory complaints.
    The name veronica is thought to be derived from the saint of that name who wiped Christ's face on his way to the cross. Some however claim that the word derives from the Greek meaning 'I bring victory', alluding of course to the herbs curative properties.

GREATER STITCHWORT. Stellaria holostea.
Medicinal part: Leaves.

Holostea or Holosteum is derived from the Greek words Holos and Osteon meaning whole and bone.
    The stems of the plant are weak and snap off at the point where the leaves are attached. The early Greeks therefore concluded that the leaves supported the stems and provided the strength against fracture. According to the Ancient Doctrine of Signatures the leaves should therefore help to heal broken bones.
    The early name, stitchwort, was attributed to this plant because it was thought to cure the stitch.
    According to Gerard 'they are wont to drink it in wine with the pouder of Acornes, against the paine in the side, stitches, and such like.'

GREAT HAIRY WILLOW HERB. Epilobium hirsutum.
Height: Two to three feet.
Medicinal part: Leaves and flowers.

The flowers produce large quantities of nectar which when soaked in wine produced an elixir which was reputed to restore an invalid near death back to health in a matter of days.
    The leaves were used in a crushed form as a poultice to wounds on the battlefield, both to stem the flow of blood and to assist with the healing process. It has since been discovered that the leaves do contain a very high concentration of vitamin C, approx. 140 mg. per 100 gms. of vegetation and it is known that ascorbic acid assists in the formation of collagen the basic protein of connective tissue.

GROUND IVY. Glechoma hederacea.
Medicinal part: Plant.

This herb bears no relationship to the true ivy.

It was used as a natural bitter flavouring until the introduction of hops in the sixteenth century.

During the brewing of ale the leaves of ground ivy or gill were added to the fermenting liquid as flavouring and to help the brew to clear, hence the name in the west country of 'ale hoof'. Its use must still have been retained in some parts well after the introduction of hops as Jonathan Swift of Gullivers Travels fame complained in 1767; 'I was forced to dine for tenpence upon gill ale, bad broth and three chops of mutton'.

It was extensively used medicinally for the treatment of bronchial complaints, and was sold on the streets of London for this purpose up until the last century.

A tonic for bronchial catarrh was made by soaking the leaves in wine, decanting, then warming the liquor before the addition of honey. Unfortunately there appears to be no record of quantities used, but I assume the honey was merely added as a sweetener to taste.

HYSSOP. Hyssopus Officinalis.
Height: 1–2 feet.
Medicinal part: Foliage and flowers.

Hyssop has been prescribed medicinally for at least 3000 years. It is a carminative, emmenagogue, expectorant, stomachic and stimulant. Immersed in wine for three days, the resultant liquor can be used to relieve chesty coughs and throat infections. With the addition of sage it is beneficial for the treatment of flatulence and a soothing lotion for inflammations and skin irritations.

LAVENDER. Lavendula Officinalis.
Height: One to two feet.
Medicinal part: Flowers and foliage.
Soak 20 gms. of the leaves and flowers in a cupful of wine for twenty four hours. Decant liquid and bottle. Protect from sunlight.

The resulting liquor is effective in the treatment of migraine headache, and dizziness, and will relieve the distress caused by vomiting and nausea.

LEMON. Citrus limon.

See wine section for medicinal properties.

LILY OF THE VALLEY. Convallaria majalis.

The use of this plant is not recommended unless prescribed as a homeopathic remedy by a qualified medical practitioner.

In ancient times the flowers were distilled in wine and the resultant distillate used for the treatment of apoplexy and dropsy.

MARJORAM, POT MARJORAM, MARJORAM HORTENSIS & ORIGANUM VULGARE.
Height: 1 to 2 feet.
Medicinal part: Plant

Used for the treatment of indigestion, headache, nervous complaints, and whooping cough. Used externally for linaments, and lotions in the treatment of varicose veins, gout, and rheumatism.

MEADOW SWEET, *FILIPENDULA ULMARIA*.
Height: Up to five feet.
Medicinal part: Foliage and flowers.

Is used in the treatment of arthritis, influenza, and rheumatism. Salicyclic acid is one of the constituents of the herb that makes it useful for treating complaints of this kind.

MINT. Mentha piperita – spicata – gentilis – rotundifolia – aqua.
Height: Up to two feet.
Medicinal part: Foliage.

All the above mints can be used as carminatives, cholagogue and stomachic.
The anodyne properties of the plant especially aqua (water) and rotundifolia (apple) make it suitable for the external application to skin ailments.

NETTLE. Urtica dioica.
Height: Up to three feet.
Medicinal part: Young leaves, roots.

See wine section for medicinal uses.
Old plants should not be used for internal medication as they can cause kidney and bowel inflammations the symptoms of which resemble poisoning.

FIELD POPPY. Papaver rhoeas.

Like all poppies it exudes a white latex from cuts in the seed case which contain various complex alkaloids. In the case of the opium poppy this latex has been used to prepare several types of drugs. The field poppy has been used in the past for many herbal remedies, which include treatment of pain gout, and St. Anthony's fire.
The use of this plant is not recommended unless prescribed by a qualified medical practitioner.
In ancient times restless infants were given a syrup made from the petals to make them sleep. But for how long?

RUE. Ruta graveolens.
Height: Up to three feet.
Medicinal part: Foliage.

Has been used to relieve rheumatic pains and eliminate intestinal worms. In olden days large doses of rue were prescribed for abortion. However it must have been a kill or cure remedy as large doses of this powerful drug are poisonous. Many people show an allergic reaction to even small doses of this herb, and it has been reported that some people with sensitive skin have developed a rash just from touching the plant.

Salvia officinalis

SAGE. Salvia officinalis.
Height: Two feet.
Medicinal part: Leaves.

In the past, sage was prescribed for nervous conditions, depression, and vertigo.
It is very effective against excess perspiration.
For laryngitis and mucous congestion steep a sprig of sage in a cupful of wine for twelve hours. Take one 5 ml. measure every two to four hours until condition clears.
For an effective inhalent in the treatment of the above, (which we as a family found highly beneficial), add a sprig of rosemary, thyme and sage in a saucepan of warm wine (boil on low heat). The inhaled vapours quickly clear blocked passages and soon restore the sense of smell.

SORREL. Rumex acetosella. and R. acetosa.
Height: One foot.
Medicinal part: Leaves and root.
R. acetos a variety once prized in this country as a vegetable. It is said that Henry VIII held it in great esteem, and ordered it to be served at every banquet. The chopped leaves were used to make a green sauce served with fish and meat dishes.
The sour sauce was served as flavouring and to mask any tainted meat or fish. The sourness is caused by oxalic acid. Culpepper claimed that the leaves of sorrel were thirst quenching, cooling, and of great use against scurvey if eaten in spring salad. The Roman legionnaires would suck the leaves of sorrel on long route marches to stave off thirst. Hence the botanical name Rumex comes from the Latin 'Rumo to suck'.
The powdered root seeped in wine had many medicinal uses, the main one being the treatment of internal haemorrhaging.

ST. JOHN'S-WORT. Hypericum perforatum.
Height: Up to three feet.
Medicinal part: Foliage.
The main medicinal use of this plant is in the treatment of nervous disorders.
The oil of the plant, removed by crushing in wine or alcohol, is a good external remedy for sores and bruises.
Another formula, for the oil extract, uses olive oil in place of wine but can take up to ten weeks to prepare.

SPURGE LAURAL. Daphne laureola.
The use of this plant is not recommended as all parts are acrid and poisonous. It does however have an intriguing medicinal history as it was once claimed to cure cancer, and is able to cure warts. Nicholas Culpepper warned that the juice was 'very offensive to the stomach and bowels' an under statement if ever there was one! A plant of the same family, native to Africa, has been used to provide a poisonous lotion for the tips of hunting arrows.
The black oval seeds of this plant were once crushed and used by physicians as a strong purgative.

THYME. Thymus vulgare.
Height: One foot.
Medicinal part: The plant.

The main medicinal uses of this plant were for respiratory problems. It is also known to be a good tonic for the nerves and stomach. It has natural antiseptic properties. The oil thymol, extracted from the plant or from an infusion in wine, can therefore be used as a natural antiseptic for wounds and irritant skin conditions.

As the oil encourages the flow of blood to the surface of the skin it is often incorporated in cosmetic or beauty preparations.

A powerful drug, so avoid excessive use over prolonged periods.

WORMWOOD. Artemisia absinthium.
Height: Up to three feet.
Medicinal part: Leaves.

When soaked in wine for seven days the resultant liquor can be used as a local anaesthetic, and is therefore useful for applying to sprains, irritations, wounds and bruises.

Mix with one tenth part pure glycerine or baby oil as a massage for the relief of pain caused by rheumatism, neuralgia and arthritis.

Internally the herb has been used to expel intestinal worms, hence it's name, and as a cardiac stimulant.

The use of this plant internally is not recommended however unless under the supervision of a qualified physician.

Cosmetics

Old ointment jars (some as late as the 1930's), were labelled with an inscription CERATUM GALEN, which dates back to the second century A.D. Galenus or Galen, as he is sometimes referred to, dealt at length with the beneficial effects of CERATUM HUMIDUM, for the treatment of various inflammatory conditions of the skin. In his 'De Simplicium Medicamentorum Temperamentis a c Facultatibus' he describes in detail a method for purifying wax, which was heated while adding large quantities of water. The resulting cream, when applied to the skin, caused the water to evaporate thus having a cooling effect.

In his tenth book of 'Methodus Medendi Vel de Morbis Curandis', he directs that one part of purified wax liquified in a pestle and mortar together with three parts rose oil (rose petals macerated with olive oil), then allowed to cool. After cooling water was continually added until no more could be taken up. Various apothecaries and chemists tried modifications and improvements over the centuries but could not improve on the ancient cream. It was reinstated in its original form as Unguentum Aqua Rosae in 1914. The B.P. 1014 formula was essentially Galens.

An approximation of the original formula is thought to be:

White Beeswax	2 ozs.
Rose oil	6 ozs.
Almond oil	5 ozs.
Borax	½ ozs.
Wine (or alcohol)	4 fluid ozs.

The wine or alcohol constituent can first be used to extract beneficial oils or chemicals from herbs, relative to the complaint requiring treatment, e.g. thyme for disinfectant before being incorporated in the cream.

Hand cream can be prepared with similar techniques and materials although mineral oil is more likely to be used these days in place of almond oil due to the cost factor.

Use the wine to extract the required chemicals from a herb or herbs. Mix 200 parts of the resulting liquor with 30 parts glycerine and 3 parts triethanolamine and heat to 80° centigrade. In a separate container warm 50 parts of mineral oil to 50° C then stir in 20 parts stearic acid and continue until all the stearic acid has dissolved in the oil. Carefully add the oil to the first mixture maintaining the temperature at 80°, stirring continuously. Allow cream to cool with occasional stirring to stop any separation of ingredients.

Wine Descriptions

ACID. Unsweet, not sour.
APRE (Ah-pr') Harsh: term often used by French wine makers to describe a young wine with too much tannin.
AROMA. Fragrance of a wine on exposure to air.
AROMATIC. Character of wine related to particular grape.
ASTRINGENT. See: APRE.
BALANCE. A balance of aroma–taste–acidity with no one aspect overriding the other.
BLIND. Cloudiness – lack of clarity.
BOUCHONE. Corkey, unfit to drink.
BOUQUET. The overall or collective effect of the various aromas exhibited by the wine.
BOUQUETÉ. Having a good bouquet.
COMPLETE. Lacking nothing.
CORSÉ. Having a lot of tannin – full bodied.
DÉLICAT. Light fine – not weak.
DOUX. Sweet unfortified – naturally sweet wine over 14% alcohol by volume.
ÉLÉGANT. Distinctive – not heavy.
ÉTÁFFÉ. Full.
FAT. Plenty of bouquet but no body.
FINESSE. Finely balanced – delicate taste.
FLOWERINESS. Light flowered bouquet.
FRANC DE GOUT. Clean tasting.
FRUITINESS. Strong smell or taste of the grape.
FRAICHE. Fresh tasting.
FULL. Large bouquet or taste.
GÉNÁREAUX. Full bodied generous wine.
GOÙT DE CAVE. Unpleasant taste.
GOÙT DE TERRAIN. Pleasant taste of the vineyard.
LÉGÈRETÉ. Lightness.
MÂCHE. Full – filling the mouth.
MADÉRIZÉ. Oxidised white wine.
MOELLEUX. Mellow yet full of flavour.
MORDANT. Biting sensation due to acidity.
OEIL DE PERDIX. Colour of a rosé wine.
PARFUMÉ. Perfurmed aroma.
SEC. Dry.
SACHÉ. Too dry or too acid.
SÈVE. Pleasant – smooth.
SOUPLESSES. Soft supple wine.
SOYEUX. Silky.
SAUVE. Full and smooth.
VELOUTE. Velvety full rich wine.

Glossary of Terms

ACESCENCE. Acidity due to excessive acetic acid.
ACETIFICATION. The bacterial process that converts alcohol to vinegar. Vinegar is dilute acetic acid CH_3. COOH.

$$\overset{\text{Acetobacter}}{\overset{\rightarrow}{CH_3.CH_2.OH + H_2O = CH_3. COOH + 2 H_2}}$$

ethanol   acetic   hydrogen
acid

ACID. All wine has acid: if too little is flat and insipid, if too much is said to be tart.
AEROBIC. Initial fermentation when yeast takes up oxygen from air content.
AFTER TASTE. Sensation which remains in mouth after sampling.
AGEING. Contrary to popular belief, all wines do not improve with age.
AIRLOCK. A device used during fermentation to exclude air, but allow carbon dioxide to escape.
ANAEROBIC. Secondary phase fermentation without air.
ATTENUATION. The degree of reduction in sugar during fermentation process.
APERITIF. An appetizer wine.
ARGOL. The crude tartar potassium of tartarate – which forms a deposit.
AUTOLYSIS. The process by which yeast acts upon itself to break down from the original composition.
BLENDING. Practice of mixing two wines of differing character to achieve balance.
BODY. A wine having some substance, as opposed to thin.
BOTTOMS. See lees.
BOUQUET. The overall aroma of a wine.
BUNG. A cork, wooden, or rubber stopper.
CAMPDEN TABLETS. A commercial tablet of sodium metabisulhphite which in contact with acid and water gives of sulphur dioxide, which in turn destroys wild yeast and bacteria, to sterilize.
CARBOY, A glass container for storage.
CARBONATED WINE. Wines made sparkling by injection of carbon dioxide.
CITRIC ACID. A naturally occurring acid contained in citrus fruits.
CREAM OF TARTAR. The white crystalline by-product of fermentation.
CRIADERA. Successive stages in the blending of sherries.
DIASTASE. An enzyme in barley that converts starch to sugar.
ENOLOGY. See oenology.
FERMENTATION. The process by which alcohol is created by enzyme action on sugars.
FILTER. The method used to extract solids and bacteria suspended in liquids.
FINING. Clearing of wine by additives.
FLOGGER. A tool or mallet for driving home corks.
FLOR. Skin on wine caused by sherry yeast.
FORTIFICATION. Increasing the alcoholic strength by the addition of spirit to the wine.
FRUCTOSE. Natural fruit sugar.

GRIST. Crushed and malted barley.

HYDROMETER. An instrument for measuring density or specific gravity of liquids.

INVERT SUGAR. Sugar that has been split into glucose and fructose. Honey and grape sugar are naturally occurring invert sugars.

LEES. Deposit of yeast and other solids formed during the process of fermentation, which settles at the bottom of the vessel.

MALT EXTRACT. A commercial product in which starch has been converted to fermentable sugar.

METABISULPHITE. See Campden tablets.

MUST. The ingredients used in the initial making.

NOGGIN. A quarter of one pint. 5 fl. ozs.

NUTRIENT. Nitrogenous and other chemical compounds used to 'feed' the yeast.

OXIDATION. The chemical combination with oxygen taken up from the air.

OENOLOGY. The science and study of wine.

PECTIN. A large sugar molecule found in fruit, and often the cause of hazes in fruit wines.

PECTOZYME. An enzyme used to break down pectin.

PRESSING. Extraction of juice from fruit.

PRIMING. The action of adding extra sugar.

PROOF. Proof spirit was the old Customs and Excise measure. It is in fact spirit containing 57.1% alc. e.g. Whisky at 70% proof contains 57.1 $\times$ 70/100 percent alcohol by volume. i.e. 40%.

RACKING. Siphoning the wine off lees.

ROPINESS. Bacterial polysacharides string together causing thickening of wine.

SIPHON. A device for the transfer of wine from one vessel to another, operating at two differing levels to utilise the force of gravity. The head (top end) must remain higher than the bottom for the siphon to work. The greater the difference the greater the head.

SPECIFIC GRAVITY. The density of a liquid compared to that of water at a given temperature and pressure. The greater the s.g. the higher the buoyancy.

SULPHITING. Adding a substance to wine such as Campden tablets, to introduce sulphur dioxide to sterilize and prevent further fermentation.

TANNIN. Occurs naturally in skins and stalks of fruit. It adds bite to a wine and is vital in such wines as claret. An excess of tannin can make a wine to estringent.

VITICULTURE. The cultivation of grape vines.

VITICULTURIST. A vine grower.

VINTNER. A maker of wine.

Trade Label Abbreviations

A	Amontillado
alc.	Alcohol
a	Anno (year)
Bbn.	Bourbon
Bord./x	Bordeaux
CE	Cuvée extra
Ch	Chateau
D	Distillery
E-B	Estate bottled
Et	Établissement
Ex	Extra
FO	Fine old
Md Ch	Mis du Château
NPU	Ne plus ultra
NV	Non vintage
pf	Proof
Saut	Sauternes
SFC	Superior fine cognac
SO	Superior old
Sup	Supérieur
VFC	Very fine cognac
Vint	Vintage
VO	Very old
VOP	Very old pale
VOT	Very old tawny
VOX	Very old Jerez
VS	Very superior
VSOP	Very superior old pale
Vue	Veuve
VVO	Very very old

Glossary of Medicinal Terms

Adjuvant – An added herb to aid the principal ingredient.
Amenorrhea – Delayed menstruation.
Analgesic – Pain killer
Antispasmodic – A drug to relieve pain-spasms.
Aperient – Gentle purgative.
Anti tussive – Treatment of coughs.
Antibiotic – Attacks micro-organisms.
Anodyne – Soothing.
Biliary stosis – Cessation of bile flow.
Calculus – Stone.
Carminative – Flatulence.
Cathartic – Laxative.
Cutaneous – Of the skin.
Demulcent – Soothing of irritated tissue.
Depurative – Cleanser or purifier.
De-toxify – Anti-toxin.
Diaphoretic – Promotes perspiration.
Diurectic – Expulsion of urine.
Emetic – Promotes vomiting.
Emmenagogue – Promotes menstrual flow.
Emmollient – Soothing agent.
Eneuresis – Incontinence.
Errhine – Agent to promote nasal discharge.
Euphoriant – Induces abnormal feeling of vigor or buoyancy.
Exanthematous – Eruptions of the skin.
Expectorant – Agent that increases production of sputum, or promotes the discharge of mucus from respiratory passages.
Febrifuge – Reduces fever.
Furbuncle – Boil.
Galactogogue – Encourage the secretion of milk.
Haematoma – A bruise containing blood.
Haemolysis – The dissolution of red blood cells.
Haemostatic – Stops bleeding.
Hyperaemea – A localised increase in blood content.
Laxative – Purgative.
Nephritic – An agent applicable to the treatment of kidney complaints.
Nervine – Soothes nerves.
Oedeama – Excessive accumulation of fluid in the subcutaneous tissues.
Oxytocic – Stimulates contraction of the uterine muscle to speed childbirth.
Pectoral – Relating to the lungs.
Resolutive – Reducing inflammation – disintegrating.
Rubefacien – Causing redness of the skin.
Sialogogue – Stimulation of saliva.
Sternutatiry – Induces sneezing.
Stomachic – Pertaining to the stomach.
Styptic – Agent to contract tissue.
Sudorific – Induces sweating.
Suppuration – Formation of puss.

Vasoconstrictor – Reduces the bore of arteries raising blood pressure.
Vasodilator – Opposite to above.
Vermifuge – Agent that destroys or expels intestinal worms.
Vesicant – Blistering agent.
Vulnerary – Healing application for wounds.

Index

Abdominal pains 90
Abbreviations: Wine 100, 103
Aching Limbs 23, 90
Achrohotrichia 76
Acids 21
Acinos Arvensis 84
Acne 74, 75
Aerobic Fermentation 27
Age Spots 32, 74
Ageing of Wine 28
Agrimony 10, 83
Ajuga Reptans 84
Alcoholism 75
Allergies 40, 62, 75, 76
Allium Schoenoprasum 86
Allontoin 31, 33, 86
Alopecia 76
Amygdolin 76
Anaerobic Fermentation 27
Analgesic: (See pain) 70
Anaesthetic 98
Anchusa Arvensis 85
Ancient Egyptians 6, 7, 12
Anemia 76
Angelica 29, 83
Angina 51, 70, 83
Anodyne 40, 54, 60, 94
Anti ageing 33, 40, 74, 76, 77
Anti-biotic 62, 69, 77, 85
Antidote 13, 31
Antiseptic 35, 46, 59, 85, 91
Antispasmodic 51, 57, 61
Antitoxin 33, 40, 62, 85
Anti-tussive (See coughs)
Aperient (see purgative)
Aphrodisiac 10, 18, 38, 58, 33, 85, 86
Apoplexy 93
Apothecaries 15
Apothecaries symbols 16
Appetite 4, 47, 48, 61, 62, 76
Apple 30, 31, 36, 76, 77, 80, 81
Appricot 33, 75, 76, 80, 81
Arginine 78
Arthritis 94, 98
Ascorbic Acid 9, 33, 76
Asthma 35, 77
Astringent 36, 41, 47, 57, 65, 69, 70, 71
Atheletes foot 39

Bacilla gracile 26
Bacteria 55
Balance 61, 58, 78
Balm 83
Banana 78, 80, 81

Banana Wine 32
Barley 32, 36, 75–77, 80, 81
Barley Wine 32
Bartsia 83
Basil 84
Bay 84
Beetroot Wine 34
Belladona 16
Bell Heather 84
Bellis Perensis 89
Benedictine 13
Bentonite 28
Betony 84
Bible 7, 12, 86
Bioflavonoids 9
Biotin 77
Birch Wine 33
Birthwort 84
Bishopwort 84
Blackberry 77, 80, 81
Blackberry Wine 35
Blackcurrant, 77, 80
Blackcurrant Wine 34
Blending Wine 28, 29
Blood clots, 77, 78, 81
Blood Pressure 13
Blood Purifier: 34, 35, 67, 83
   (See also Depurative)
Blois, Peter 9
Blueberry 75, 77, 81
Blueberry Wine 36
Boiling water
Boils 36, 46, 48, 57, 74
Bottling 29
British Museum 12
Broccoli 75
Broccoli Wine 36
Bronchial Disorders 32, 33, 40, 76, 93
Bruises 32, 57, 84, 86, 91, 98
Buffer chemicals 11
Bugle 84
Bugloss 85
Bullace Wine 36
Burdock 85
Burns 76, 77

Califerol 77
Calcium 28, 78, 80
Campden Tablets 19, 28
Cancer 76, 77, 97
Caraway 12, 85
Carbonic maceration 23, 25
Carbuncles 74
Cardiac 13, 49, 65, 98

Carminative   32, 47, 48, 59–61, 68, 86, 93–4
Carotene   74
Carrot   75, 76, 80, 81, 85
Carrot Wine   37
Cathartic   42, 44, 60
Cattarrh   40
Celery Wine   36
Ceratum Galen   99
Chamaelum Nobile   85
Chamomile   83, 85
Champagne   46
Chartreuse   14
Chemical additives   7
Cherry   76, 80, 81
Cherry Wine   38
Chicory   75
Childbirth   84
Chilblains   31, 77
China   12
Chives   86
Chlorine   80
Cholesterol   10, 30, 34, 75–6
Cholagogue   40, 57, 94
Cinchona   16
Cirsium Arvense   89
Classes of Wine   29
Cleaner   22
Clover Wine   39, 77
Cold   36, 40, 44, 47, 55, 68
Cold sores   89
Coles, William   85
Colitis
Collagen   90
Coltsfoot   80
Coltsfoot Wine   40
Comfrey   33, 76
Convalescence   37
Convallaria Majalis   93
Coriander   12, 86
Coughs   32, 40, 47, 55, 86, 93
Cosmetics   98–9
Cowslip   40, 75, 86
Cowslip Wine   40
Crab Apple Wine   40
Cranberry   75
Cranberry Wine   41
Creeping Thistle   89
Cromwell, Oliver   71
Culpepper, Nicholas   14, 48, 50–51, 57, 62, 71, 89, 97
Customs & Excise   19
Cyanocobalomin   76
Cystitis   10

Daisy   89
Damson Wine   41
Dandelion   75, 77, 89
Dandelion Wine   42
Daphne Laureola   97

Dark Ages   7
Date   75, 80, 81
Date Wine   43
Daucus Carotin   85
De-materia Medica   13
De-Antidotis   13
Delirium Tremens   75
Demulcent   40, 46, 47, 61, 62, 70
Depression   89, 97
Depurative   32, 61
Descriptions of Wine   100
Diarrhoea   56, 63, 65
Diaphoretic   41, 44, 46–48, 57
Digestion   83, 84, 86
Digitalis   13, 90
Dill   16
Dioscorides   13, 85
Direct Fermentation   23, 24
Distillation   19
Diurectic   10, 37, 40, 41, 44, 46, 51, 54, 57, 59, 60, 68, 69, 70, 83
Draco   12
Dropsy   49, 59, 93
Drosophilla   9
Drugs Synthectic   9
Dysentery   86
Dyspepsia   40

Echium Vulgars   85
Egyptians – Ancient   7, 12, 15
Elderberry   25, 77, 80
Elderberry Port   45
Elderberry Wine   44
Elderflower Wine   46
Elderflower Champagne   46
Eleonor of Acquitiane   9
Elm   89
Emmenagogue   57, 59, 93
  (See also Mensturation)
Emollient   40, 47
Emphysemia   74
Enuresis   10
Ephedrine   12
Epilobium Hirsutum   90
Epitherial Tissue   31, 32, 36
Equipment   19
Ergosterol   77
Ergot   16
Erica Cineria   84
Euphoriant   48
Evening Primrose   89
Exhaustion   67, 77, 86
Expectorant   40, 59, 61, 93
Eye Remedies   74, 75

Faults   73
Febrifuge   10, 54, 55, 62, 65
Fennel   16, 90
Fermentation   12, 27, 28
Fever (See Febrifuge)

Fibrositis 77
Fig 75, 80, 81
Fig Wine 47
Filisendula Ulmaria 94
Filtering 5
Finnings 21
Flatulence 37, 47, 85, 93
Flavouring 93
Foeniculum Vulgare 90
Folic Acid 31, 77
Fortifying 29
Foxglove 13, 16, 90
Flu 44, 47, 94
Fruit Juices 24
Furbuncle (see boils)

Galactagogue 58, 60
(See also Lactation)
Galen 13, 30, 58, 62, 71, 99
Gargle 41, 59, 65, 66, 69, 85, 90
Gamma Linoleic Acid 31
Garlic 14
Gastro-intestinal Disorders 37, 39, 57, 65, 76
Gerard, John 14, 63, 90
Germander Speedwell 90
Ginger Wine 47
Glass – coloured 29
Glechoma Hederacea 93
Glossary 104
Glycerine 33
Goiter 80
Golden Rod 48
Golden Rod Wine 46
Gooseberry Wine 49
Gorse flower 50
Grape 20
Grape Wine 50
Grape Concentrate 20
Grape Vine Wine 50
Grape Brandy 29
Greater Stitchwort 90
Great Hairy Willow Herb 90
Greece – Ancient 7, 12
Greengage Wine 51
Grete Herbal 14
Ground Ivy 93
Gout 44, 49

Hair loss 58, 75–77
Halitosis 31
Hawthorn Blossom Wine 51
Headache 10, 40, 44, 63, 69, 85, 94
Haemorrhage 78, 86, 97
Haemostatic 62
Heart Stimulent (See Cardiac)
Hematuria 86
Henbane 16
Henry II 9
Heroes 75

High Density Lipo Proteins 10
Hippocrates 6, 12, 13, 15
History – Herbal Medicines 11–17
History Wine 7
Homoeopathy 11
Honey 27
Hop Wine 54
Hydrogen Chloride 80
Hydrometer 26–27
Hygroscopic 33
Hypericum Perforatum 97
Hyperthoiroidism 75
Hyperthrodoxin 74
Hypnotic 54
Hyssop 93

Imperial Weights 73
Impetigo 57, 74
Indigestion 47, 85, 94
Infertility 78
Inflamation 40, 93
Influenza (See Flu)
Infusion 23–24
Ingredients 20
Inisitol 77
Inorganic 11
Insect Bites 40, 48, 84
Insomnia 40, 51, 54, 83, 84
Invent Sugar 27
Iodine 80
Iron 80

Jaundice 10, 32, 50, 59
Juice Extraction 24

Kidney Treatment 32, 56, 59, 68, 84
Konakion 29, 78

Label Abbreviations 103
Labelling bottles 29
Lactation 58, 80, 84
Lactic Acid 28
Lactuca Sativa 93
Lady's Mantle 33
Laetrile 76
Laryngitis 97
Laurel Bay 12, 84
Lavender 93
Laxative 41, 47, 61, 62, 65
(See also Purgative)
Leg Ulcer 40
Lemon 77, 78, 80, 81
Lemon Wine 54
Lemon Balm 83
Leucorrhea 86
Lily of the Valley 93
Lime Blossom Wine 55
Lipo-proteins 10
Liver remedies 32, 39, 70, 76, 81, 84
Liverwort 10, 83

Loganberry Wine 55
Lysine 78

Macedonia – King of 12
Magnesium 28, 78, 80
Ma-huang 12
Malic Acid 30
Malo-Lactic 28
Malt Wine 56
Mandrakes 12
Manganese 81
Marigold 33
Marigold Wine 56
Marjoram 94
Marrow Wine 57
Massage Oil 33
Maturation (See post fermentation)
May Blossom 51
Meadowsweet 10, 94
Melancholia 12–13, 85
Melissa Officianalis 83
Menopause 77
Menstrual Disorders 37, 59, 76, 78, 86
Mentha Piperita 94
Mentha Spicato 94
Mentha Gentilis 94
Mentha Aqua 94
Methyl Alcohol 9
Metric conversion 72
Migraine 40, 63, 75, 93
Minerals 80–81
Mint 16, 81, 94
Molybdenum
Monks 6, 13, 67
Mouth Wash 59, 66, 85
Muscular Development 76, 80
Muscular Dystrophy 76
Must: definition of 21
Must: preparation 23
Must: varieties 23

Narcotic (See poppy)
Natural Ingredients 72
Nausea 76, 84, 93
Nervine (See Nervous disorders)
Nervous disorders 37, 40, 61, 69, 71, 76, 89,
94, 97
Nettle Wine 58
Nettle 31, 33, 75, 77, 81, 94
Neuralgia 55, 75, 98
Niacin (See Nicitinic Acid)
Nicotinic Acid 75
Noah 7

Oak Leaf Wine 58
Odontis Verna 83
Oenothera Biennis 89
Opium 16
Orange 75, 77, 78, 80, 81
Organic definition 11

Origanum Vulgare 94
Orotic Acid 31
Oxytocic 63
(See also Pregnancy)

Pain Relief 83, 94
Pain – Stitch 90
Panothenic Acid 76
Papaver Rhoeas 94
Papyrus documents 14
Para – Aminobenzic Acid (PABA) 77
Parkinsons Disease 76
Parliament Acts of 15
Parsley 75
Parsley Wine 59
Parsnip 75, 80
Parsnip Wine 60
Pasteur, Louis 14
Pea Pod 75, 80, 81
Pea Pod Wine 61
Pear Wine 62
Pectin 23
Peppermint 16
Pharyngitis 59
Pharmaceutical – Society 15
Pharoahs 6
Phlebitis 40
Phosphorous 81
Pineapple 75
Pleurisy 51
Plum 76, 80
Plum Wine 62
Poppy (field) 94
Port 29
Potassium 35, 78, 81
Potassium Cyanide 11
Potassium Sorbate 19, 28
Potato 75, 76, 80, 81
Potato Wine 63
Pregnancy 77, 80, 81
Preparation of Must 20, 26
Proteins 78, 80–81
Prothombrin 78
Prune Wine 64
Pulp fermentation 23, 25
Purgative 39, 41, 44, 53, 59, 62, 65, 69, 97
Pyridoxine (See Vitamin B6)

Quinine 16

Radiation 76
Raisins 75, 80, 81
Raisin Wine 64
Rash 65
Raspberry 77, 80
Raspberry Wine 64
Rauwolfia Serpentine 13
Records – Wine 7
Redcurrant 75
Redcurrant Wine 65

Remedies Wine 73
Renal Colic 68
Rheumatism 42, 44, 46, 58, 59, 68, 70, 76, 94, 96, 98
Rheumatic fever 84
Rhubarb Wine 66
Riboflavin
Rice 68, 75, 76
Rice Wine 67
Rickets 77
Ringworm 71
Romans: Early 7, 12, 13
Rosehips 9, 68, 77, 80
Rosehip Wine 68
Rosemary 29
Rose petal Wine 69
Roundworm 35
Rue 94
Rumex Acetosella 97
Ruta Graveolena 94

Sage 29, 97
Salicylic Acid 10
Salvia Officianalis 97
Sal Voltile 16
Scurvy 76
Sea Sickness 75
Sedative 49, 51, 54, 61, 85
Serpisil 11
Sialagogue 46, 47, 65
Side effects 10
Skin Problems 33, 38, 43, 46, 71, 75, 89, 93, 94
Sleep 40, 51, 78
Sloe Wine 69
Snake bite 84, 85
Soaking ingredients 23, 25
Sodium 80, 81
Sores 65, 97
Sore Throat 68, 69
Sorrel 97
Spasmophylia 77
Spearmint 75
Specific Gravity 27
Spleen 50
Sprains 32, 57, 98
Spurge Laurel 97
Stabilising 28–29
Stachys Officianalis 84
Starch 63
Stellaria Holostea 90
Sterilization 22
St. John's Wort 97
Stimulant 42, 44, 48, 59, 71, 91, 93
Stomachic 41, 60–62, 65, 69
Storing
Strawberry 77
Strawberry Wine 70
Stress 86

Sudorific 57
Sugar Beet Wine 34
Sugar Extraction 23, 24
Sulphur 81
Sumarians 12

Tannin 59
Taraxacum Officianalis 89
Tea 71
Tea Wine 70
Tetany 77
Theophrastus 13
Theriacs 13
Thirst 97
Thyme 12, 33
Tinnitus 75
Tocupheral 77
Tonic 41, 48, 54, 70, 71
Tonsillitis 59
Toothache 69, 83
Trade Abbreviations 103
Tragus 59
Tranquilizer 85
Traumatic decoction 84
Trytophants 78
Tuberculosis 69
Tyrosine 78

Ulcerated Gum 48, 59
Ulcerated Stomach 57, 63
Ulcers 38, 74, 84, 86
Ulmas – Glabra & Procea 89
Urtica Dioica 94

Vasoconstrictor 105
Vasodilator 46
Vermifuge 55, 61, 62, 68, 94, 98
Vesicant 94
Veronica Officianalis 90
Vertigo 51, 75, 97
Vipers Bugloss 85
Vitamin A 40, 74, 77
Vitamin B_1 29, 42, 43, 75
Vitamin B_2 42, 43, 75
Vitamin B_3 75
Vitamin B_5 76
Vitamin B_6 76, 78
Vitamin B_{12} 76
Vitamin B_{17} 76
Vitamin C 9, 35, 42, 68, 76, 78, 90
Vitamin D 77
Vitamin E 31, 42, 77
Vitamin H 77
Vitamin K 31, 42, 78
Vitamin P 77
Volatile Oils 29
Vulnerary (See Wounds)

Warts 57, 97
Wheat 75, 81

Wheat Wine   71
Whooping Cough   94
Willow Bark   10
Wine Descriptions   100
Worms: Intestinal
    (See Vermifuge)

Wort   10
Wounds   48, 62, 76, 78, 84, 86, 980, 97, 98

Yeast   14, 75, 76, 77

Zinc   78, 81

Pub Walks series

PUB WALKS IN DORSET

FORTY MORE PUB WALKS IN DORSET

PUB WALKS IN HAMPSHIRE AND I.O.W.

PUB WALKS IN WEST SUSSEX

PUB WALKS IN DEVON.

PUB WALKS IN CORNWALL.